D1104276

SHEARWATERS

SHEARWATERS

BY THE SAME AUTHOR

I KNOW AN ISLAND
EARLY MORNING ISLAND
A POT OF SMOKE
THE WAY TO AN ISLAND
LETTERS FROM SKOKHOLM
ETC.

Caroline was a good mother

SHEARWATERS

R. M. LOCKLEY

LONDON: J. M. DENT & SONS LTD

This book is copyright. It may not be reproduced whole or in part by any method without written permission. Application should be made to the publishers:

J. M. DENT & SONS LTD.
Aldine House · Bedford St. · London

Made in Great Britain
by
The Temple Press · Letchworth · Herts.
First published 1942
Reprinted 1942, 1947

V 67/3 m

CONTENTS

ILLUSTRATIONS

INTRODUCTION

THOSE who built the little house on Skokholm—and the thick walls of the central room may have been built in the thirteenth century—selected a site which both protected the occupants from the heavy southerly winds and enabled them to watch the coming and going of any boat between the island and the mainland. Thus, from the north side of the house, the island slopes to the sea, giving an unobstructed view of Jack Sound, that narrow neck through which the silver currents pour and through which the red sails of the fishing boats must always pass. But the north wind, though at times it blows coldly about the house, is never so violent as the south wind.

On the south side of the house the view is immediately obscured by a rocky knoll rising higher than our single tall chimney. This knoll breaks the force of the prevalent southerly gales; so that from the south door of the house you look upon a green slope interspersed with red sandstone outcrops which are marbled with grey and yellow and white lichens. There is trace of an old ramp, or enclosure, crowning the little knoll, but it is scarcely discernible even under the thin growth of moss, allseed, sheep's sorrel, and fine grass. Here and there are bluebells, and in autumn a few wind-torn blackberries show the pale dyes of their petals—though they seldom fruit. And after midsummer the wood-sage plentifully nods its waxy bells in the tireless wind-eddies.

The pasture of the knoll is poor, as much through overgrazing by rabbits as through springing solely from a thin layer of peat over the infertile rock. But there are one or two hollows overlaid with perhaps a foot depth of this friable peat. One such pocket faces the house; is, indeed, only a dozen paces from our south door. And in this hollow some six pairs of Manx shearwaters have their nesting burrows.

Nothing could have been more convenient for my purpose than to select this group for study. Like the martins in the eaves of a country house, the shearwaters of this knoll were intimately with us throughout the summer. Their cries were loudest of all island noises at night. I had only to slip out of the door each evening, walk a few paces, and, with the aid of a torch and a note-book, examine and note the movements of the individuals in this colony.

I hope I have not made it sound too easy. Not every one has the luck to live on, to have an island to himself. It is true that before I could start this ten years' study of the shearwater there were certain formalities to be got through. I wished to settle on this remote Welsh island in order to live simply and undisturbed and alone, but in the company of those things I most cared for: wild birds and animals, wild flowers, the sea, and a wide horizon. But Skokholm is no tropic isle where you can walk naked in perpetual sunshine, pluck your food from a bread-fruit tree, and take your drink from a coco-nut shell. Skokholm's two hundred and forty-two acres lie in the path of a fierce tidal stream and in a latitude subject to heavy westerly and southerly gales. There is little shelter on the island, which is no more than a grassy treeless plateau, rock-bound, and raised about one hundred feet above the sea. Here and there on its surface are jagged outcrops of rock such as the knoll, these providing but scant shelter, according to the direction of the wind.

Others had struggled to live here in bygone days, and left the mark of their labour in the shape of ruined buildings, and stone-walled boundaries to fields now overrun with rabbits, weeds, and bracken. But as a colonist man has been no more than sporadic. Loneliness and marketing problems defeated him time and again. When I discovered the island it had been unoccupied for at least twenty years; nor had the last tenant done more than re-roof some of the outbuildings (but he had taken the sheet iron away with him on leaving). I found blackbirds, dunnocks, swallows, pipits, and storm-petrels nesting in the roofless house, stable, and barn. Birds are ever the true, the constant freeholders of Skokholm.

However, I myself did not propose to set up anything so cumbrous and unremitting as a *farm* on the island. I had neither the inclination nor the capital for such an undertaking. All I cared was to fit into the environment, to build, like the birds, a weather-proof shelter or nest sufficient for my immediate needs; and to obtain, like the birds, a plain living from the island and the sea around it. There might, or might not, be some leisure moments, but if there were I should use them, as I had always used such moments, in watching birds. As it happened, there was very little spare time for this study in the first summer, during which I was occupied in restoring the old farmhouse on the island, using material from the opportunely (for me) wrecked schooner *Alice Williams*.

Elsewhere[1] I have described the work of that first year, and how I found the island, and settled there, was married, and became a shepherd, with nothing to think of but my island and its precious contents: my wife and home, my sheep and garden, my boat, the sea, the weather, and the wild birds. In this book I tell how, with my wife's help —for we were alone in that second summer—we began to study the birds of Skokholm individually, and in particular the members of the shearwater colony outside our back door. R. M. L.

SKOKHOLM,
    PEMBROKESHIRE

[1] *The Way to an Island.* Dent, 1941.

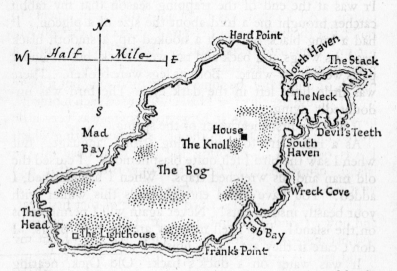

Skokholm, showing the areas (shaded) where the concentrations of breeding shearwaters are heaviest. The unshaded area is also occupied by smaller and more scattered groups of shearwaters

CHAPTER I

It was at the end of the trapping season that my rabbit catcher brought me a bird about the size of a pigeon. It had a long black bill with a hooked tip, a smooth black head, its wings and back and tail were black, but its under parts were snow-white. Both its legs were broken. There was little light left in the dark eye. The bird was undoubtedly dying.

It was the first shearwater of the spring.

As a rule I try to avoid using strong language. But when I saw the bird I felt quite blasphemous. I cursed the old man and his wretched traps. When I had finished, I added: 'You have killed enough birds this winter with your beastly instruments! Never again will I permit traps on the island! Don't tell me they are the best things. I don't care if they are. I'm finished with them!'

It was water on a duck's back. Old Dick, nearing seventy, if he heard distinctly (for he was rather deaf), cared less for my feelings than for those of the bird. He continued to stroke the bird, quietly muttering to himself: 'Oh, you poor cocklolly, you poor dear, did the trap hurt you then?'

He sighed as he pulled the bird's neck to put it from further suffering. He was genuinely sorry for the bird. He took a great interest in birds. He thought that I would like to see this first shearwater of the year. He was particularly fond of small and harmless birds. Larger, more rapacious birds he disliked, because he feared the harm they could do to his rabbits and to small birds in his traps. Only the other day he had found a buzzard in his traps,

I

and stupidly he had killed it with one blow of his trapping-paddle. He had said it had attacked him with its wings . . . 'a great eagle of a bird, sir!'

The old man had been a trapper all his life, and his outlook was coloured accordingly. It was surprising that he still had a thought for the suffering of a trapped bird. This and a certain noble dignity of carriage and address made you like the old rascal. He had almost a passionate love of Skokholm. He was altogether an unusual figure, and something of an ascetic. Money worried him very little, and as for food, if he was working far from the house, at the other end of the island, he never troubled to come home to the midday meal. He preferred to tighten his belt and work on. When he returned at night he would sit close to the fire, poking it so that it never stopped blazing, and every now and then announcing some bird or ship or incident of weather or work which came to his mind as he recalled the hours he had spent at his task that day. Often, his mind wandering, he retold an incident which had happened days before.

But I was tired of the wholesale slaughter of birds in rabbit traps. I wished I had not been advised to use them. How was I, fresh from an inland district of Monmouth-shire, where rabbits were scarce and steel-jawed traps—to my knowledge—never used, to know that these instruments took wholesale toll of wild birds? I was to learn from bitter experience that on an island as wind-swept as Skokholm birds used rabbit holes freely in lieu of better shelter. Every bird that trod on the fresh earth—and many were naturally attracted by it—covering the pan of a trap placed in the mouth of a rabbit hole was doomed to broken legs and, since a bird with broken legs might as well be dead, a cruel death.

At first Dick had hidden from me the birds he had caught, but later I got wind of the slaughter. I had found him roasting blackbirds and thrushes over the driftwood fire of his room in the cottage. After that I had made it a rule to go round with him whenever I could spare the time in the early morning. And while he collected the rabbits from the traps I picked up a grim harvest of thrushes, blackbirds, redwings, pipits, dunnocks, stonechats, starlings, lapwings, turnstones, curlews, woodcock, snipe, even little owls, oyster-catchers, and fieldfares. Why, even a wren or a mouse or frog would spring these traps, so delicately, so expertly, did Dick set them.

Well, it was finished now. The first shearwater was back on the island. To-morrow night, probably, scores of them would arrive.

I took the shearwater from Dick's hand. I would have to dismiss the old man now. But I spoke softly. After all, it was I, as master, who was to blame for using traps.

I said: 'The cocklollies have come home. That means we finish the rabbiting for the season. Pull up the traps, wash them, oil them, and put them away. Then I'll put you ashore, Dick, and you can dig your garden and set your early potatoes in good time.'

It was February the second. I had seen a primrose in the shelter of the harbour, and I was longing for the spring which I could feel in my bones. . . .

What should I do with the dead shearwater? Few ornithologists had the chance to handle a shearwater so early in the year. It might be worth sending it up to an expert for examination, to some specialist who would report on its condition, moult, breeding organs, etc. I myself was only an amateur field naturalist and knew little of these things. It seemed a better fate for the bird than to throw it away to the eager gulls and crows.

I sent it to the editor of the periodical *British Birds*. H. F. Witherby replied:

Manx shearwater was interesting. Female. Ova well-formed, oviduct bulged in two places and undoubtedly a bird which had laid egg or eggs in its time—therefore adult! I mean, *not* a bird born last year. Nothing in stomach. Moult considerable on neck, throat, and head. . . .

Astonishing information to a young inexperienced ornithologist!

But more was to come from the discerning editor. In another letter he wrote:

The exact incubation period of the Manx shearwater is not known. It would be a good piece of work if you could observe this, and the exact fledging period. A record of a number of individuals would be safest and most valuable. Would ringing help you in this?

I gladly accepted his offer to send me numbered aluminium leg rings with which I could identify individual birds. But I did not realize that in accepting the offer I was completely revolutionizing my haphazard method of studying birds, which was that of the average observer who writes in his note-book: 'March 26th, first chiffchaff heard. April 12th, cuckoo and swallow here . . .' and leaves it at that. Only by the use of rings is it possible to become a close student of the individual bird and to know it year after year.

At that time Witherby was making and supplying these rings himself, but recently he has turned this organization over to the British Trust for Ornithology, and now all rings bear the address of the British Museum, Natural History, London.

*   *   *   *   *

Man is accustomed to think and speak of the sea-birds plurally, lumping them together in flocks, hosts, crowds, and so on. Certainly it was easy for me to do this in the case of the Manx shearwater. Before I came to Skokholm I had only seen the bird in flocks off the coast of Lundy Island in the Bristol Channel. There they had all been flying north towards Skokholm and Skomer, their great breeding ground in the west. I have never been able to find out whether the Manx shearwater breeds on Lundy, but lighthouse keepers have assured me that they have often heard the birds 'singing' at night there, and occasionally they have found a nest. It may be that, as in the Isle of Man, where the species was first named, they have more or less abandoned Lundy on account of the rats which infest that island. Howbeit, after those flocks off Lundy, and a night with the shearwaters at Skomer, the sister island lying two miles or so north of Skokholm, I suddenly found myself master of this island of Skokholm and its ten thousand pairs of shearwaters.

Ten thousand. That was my first rough estimate of their numbers on Skokholm's 242 acres. In the day-time all you saw of them was a sprinkling of corpses at the rate of about six to the acre over the whole island. These unlucky ones had been slain by the great black-backed gulls and were now no more than inverted skins—perhaps, if the gull had been voracious, only wings and breast-bone.

But on dark nights in the spring and summer the shearwaters appeared, coming out from their holes in the ground and joining together in a bedlam of weird screaming. There seemed at first no intelligence in that wild howling —it was the crying of insane spirits wandering without aim or restraint over the rough rocks and the bare pastures. Indeed I cannot now properly describe that noise of the shearwater. I once got some friends to write on slips of paper what they considered was a phonetic rendering of a typical individual scream of the Manx shearwater. We then exchanged slips and each read aloud the other's rendering. The result was amusing but unconvincing. Then we tried similes. 'Like the crow of a throaty rooster whose head is chopped off before the last long note has fairly begun,' was judged the best. And I will leave it at that.

The Manx shearwater, then, was to me little more than a strange nocturnal noise, as strange and mysterious as the cuckoo's wandering voice was to the earliest naturalists. By day I could see those dried-up skins, and if I chose to go out with a torch at night I could discern the black and white forms scuttling about the holes and warrens inside which the single egg would be laid and the chick hatched and reared.

I turned to Witherby's *Practical Handbook of British Birds* for enlightenment. There I read that the Manx shearwater is

sometimes seen at rest on the water, but comes under notice oftenest as it careers over surface of sea. A few rapid beats alternate with periods of sailing with long narrow wings quite rigid, dead black of back in view at one moment, pure white underparts at next, as body is tilted at right angles and tip of lower wing seems almost to cut the waves. Obtains some of its food by diving, but bulk from surface, and in picking it up the bird often paddles with its feet as smaller petrels do. Silent except after dark at breeding places, where there is a babel of varying sounds, some harsh, some soft and crooning. . . . Breeds in colonies, sometimes making its burrow in low-lying islands, or at times in grassy slopes on face of cliffs. Nest, merely a little dry grass in some cases at end of burrow. Egg, one only, white. Breeding season: from early May to first half June. Incubation: by both sexes; period unknown, but estimated at a month (Hantzsch). Single brooded.

The breeding season began in early May, did it? Then why should the rabbit catcher trap a female in a rabbit hole on the second of February? And this female, Witherby has said, was undoubtedly a bird which had laid eggs in other seasons. It was an *old* adult.

I was puzzled. Like the rook which pays an early spring call to the rookery, did the shearwater come home to indulge in a little house - hunting, to spring - clean the burrow against the coming season, perhaps to eject the rabbits which had found a dry roof there all the winter through?

At least her arrival was not accidental. Since that day many other shearwaters had been paying visits on dark February nights. They screamed more and more often as they flew in increasing numbers over the roof of the house, joining with the loud whickering of the oyster-catchers which, too, were paying surreptitious night visits to their nesting territories. By day, however, the shearwaters were at sea, and the oyster-catchers stood on the rocks by the edge of the tide, their carmine legs like stilts, their blood-orange bills thrust in their scapulars, their vermilion irides hidden in sleep; their demeanour suggesting that they knew nothing of the outrageous skirmishing which the island meadow had witnessed in the night.

Spring was on her way even to this naked rabbit-ridden wind-swept island. The frogs had spawned in the ponds where the wild ducks had enjoyed sanctuary all winter through. The leaves of the primrose and lords and ladies were beginning to uncurl in the increasing sunshine. The milch goat sought the sheltered east slopes of the island where the glaucous leaves of the sea-campion provided succulent grazing. The skylark, the song-thrush, and the dunnock sang by day, the oyster-catcher and the shearwater screeched by night.

Suddenly spring was thrust back. On 15th February we awoke to find a heavy snowstorm raging. The island was white with a foot depth of snow, here and there blown into deeper drifts by a furious east wind. The in-shore sea by contrast was a dirty yellow, and off shore the water was a muddy grey.

The salt in the air gradually melted the snow. In four days there was none left. But the ground remained hard.

On the mainland roads were impassable for many days, telegraph poles and trees were down, and transport dislocated. Driven before the icy wind and by cold and hunger, thousands of birds now began to arrive on the frozen island. Starlings, redwings, and song-thrushes alighted on the edge, lost their balance, staggered, and rolled over, feet in air, dead as the proverbial door nail. Many fell into the sea, too weak to fly up over the cliffs. Robins and black-birds could scarcely hop to the door of our cottage. Some, including a female chaffinch blind in one eye, edged their way into the buildings to receive a dole of bread-crumbs and chicken-feed which we in pity issued to them. Field-fares, larks, lapwings, golden plover, and snipe stood or lay

still, under our windows and on our doorstep, too feeble
to move. The ravens, crows, and gulls walked about
among them, pulling off the heads and devouring the
viscera, but not troubling to pick the wasted framework.

The more lively individuals of the starling hordes pushed
a way into the hutches of some tame rabbits in an enclosed
warren, and slept warmly at night among the families of
suckling conies, while the rest of the starlings crept at night
into rabbit holes and down our chimney. Few of them
awoke to earthly morning again. At night we heard no
shearwaters, but only the honking of wild geese, and in the
morning I noticed their droppings in the frozen grass. In
the east bays, when we collected the wood abundantly
drifting in on the cold breezes, we found bundles of
drowned land birds sprinkled along the edge of the tide.

In all this period—and the exceptional frosts lasted a
month—the shearwaters had forsaken the island. Perhaps
the continuous low temperature had cooled the ardour of
the home-hunting shearwater, just as it had silenced the
spring songs of the small land birds.

Early in March the bitter east winds dropped. Calm
dark nights intervened. The shearwaters suddenly returned
from their perpetual refuge, the sea. And thereafter an
occasional white frost had no power to stop their nightly
arrival.

Salmon

Shearwaters assembling at sunset

Salmon

The sun has set and the flock is restless to be on land

CHAPTER II

EACH evening the shearwaters gathered on the water to the north and north-west of the island, between Skokholm and Skomer. As the sun slowly sank behind the lonely island of Grassholm the great rafts of shearwaters would rise and skim in circles and figures of eight, waiting restlessly for darkness.

The flocks would swing as one being, their white breasts now a silver flash in the sun's last rays, and then, as their dark upper parts were simultaneously presented, they showed velvet-black on the grey-blue sea. They would settle on the water again, so that from the island cliffs a mile distant we could barely discern the united host—it was merely a cloud shadow, a black streak like a puff of wind or a vein of the tide on calm water. But soon, ever restless, they would rise, wheel, and perhaps split up for a while, making three or four separate flocks. And always these grew in size as more and more birds came gliding in from oceanic feeding grounds to the north and west and south. A long unending line of individuals, for instance, streamed around the western headland of Skokholm for as long as you could see in the failing light.

Later in the spring the assembly was often half a mile long and perhaps a furlong broad—rough measurements obtained by taking bearings between island and island. It contained probably more than a hundred thousand shearwaters. Of course not all of these were breeding at Skokholm; the majority had their homes in burrows on the sister island of Skomer, which is about three times as big as Skokholm.

Waiting, waiting, waiting—what are the birds doing in those great rafts all the evening? Does their impatience and herd excitement force them to scream as on land? Assembling always in the same spot so many hours each evening before attempting to land, they surely must be doing something important? Yet with powerful glasses, from the cliffs, I can only see a complete idleness, apart from the leisurely flighting to and fro.

On those fine spring evenings my wife and I sometimes launched the boat and sailed through the shearwater assembly, excusing ourselves for this pleasure on the pretext of trailing a line for pollack.

As our red sail slowly bore down on the chequered carpet we could hear nothing but the ripple of the water under the boat's stem and the creak of the mast where it fitted loosely against the thwart. The shearwaters were quite silent. They were tame, and seemed to be reluctant to move out of our way. None of them was feeding. Perhaps they were less hungry for food than for the island and all it signified for them at that season.

Having assembled while the sun was still well above the horizon, what prevents the shearwater flying to the land and diving straight into its hole, as does the puffin? Why is the shearwater so strictly nocturnal on land? Can it be that it fears an attack by the great black-backed gull? Certainly enough shearwater corpses lie strewn all over the island—the great gull dines all too often on this species. But there are also many remains of the puffin where this gull has banqueted. The great gull is not particular. He cunningly lies in wait at the mouth of a burrow, seizing anything that is unlucky enough to emerge, bird or rabbit. So the shearwater on land would only run the same risk as the puffin, which after all is a smaller bird, though apparently a more courageous one. The shearwater refuses to take the risk.

In one text-book I read an explanation: 'The Manx shearwater is a strictly nocturnal bird and if taken out of its burrow in daylight is quite dazed and helpless.' Now as to the 'strictly nocturnal' part, here we are in a boat sailing through the great flock of shearwaters with the sun still above the horizon and a light on the water so dazzling that we half-close our eyes to protect them from the glare. Consider, what more fierce light in the world is there than the sun reflected on the mirror of the sea at noon? Yet the shearwater lives on the sea as well at noon as at midnight; indeed, we have seen that it is often on land at midnight and at sea at noon. So that part of the explanation is worthless, without a qualifying 'while on land.' Also the shearwater is certainly not 'dazed' by the sun, for it must be able to see perfectly by day, although perhaps for a second when dragged from a dark hole into the sunlight it might appear confused; in such circumstances, as man knows from experience, the eye needs a moment to adjust itself to the flood of light.

'Helpless'—ah, now we are on the track of something more promising. While the puffin is an expert walker and can even run upright on its orange-webbed feet, the shearwater is a real blunderer on land. Its feet are placed so far back behind the heavy breast that dignified biped progress on land is impossible. These feet are really a pair of propellers, twin screws which, as our sail rides through the flock that evening, are successfully used to drive the thousands of black and white feathered boats about us at speed.

When we got back that evening I collected some shearwaters as soon as it was quite dark, and brought them into the house to study their locomotion on land. Of course, in so narrow a space as our humble living-room they could not, with those narrow wings, get up enough speed to take off into the air. And they did not even try. They were unable to stand upright at all. They rested quietly with their breasts on the floor. Apparently they were not to be disturbed easily, were quite phlegmatic about their capture and treatment under artificial light. When gently urged to move on they rose unsteadily, made a waddling run upright on their toes, their sharp wings slightly fluttering, and then suddenly subsided flat on their breasts. The performance reminded me of the walk of a rather frightened top-heavy farm duck. The bright beady chocolate eye looked inquiringly at me as if to say: 'Have done with all this tomfoolery and let me out into the decent night. You can see I'm not adapted to walking, but at least I can shuffle along. I can swim on the sea, I can fly in the air, and I can also move under the water, which is more than you can do, my tormentor.'

It appears at first as if the birds had grasped the situation in one glance—they were enclosed in a prison which did not allow of a sufficiently long run for taking off into the air, therefore it was better to stay and await events. But was this really intelligence? Were the shearwaters capable of thinking all I have made them seem to say?

Let us see what happens when that fellow-sharer of the rabbit burrows, the puffin, is placed in the room. Since the puffin is diurnal when on land, we had better put him in the room in daylight. Of course his narrow little wings, too, prevent him from flying without a fairly long run for a take-off.

Hallo! Mr Puffin—as the fishermen call him—lives up to his reputation as a lively inquisitive bird by immediately and rapidly pattering around the room. He seems to be looking for some hole to hide in, or possibly some exit to freedom. In and out, under the settle, the chest, the desk, the arm-chairs, he nervously patters, thrusting into corners with his rainbow parrot beak. It is a long time before he despairs of finding a way out. At last he subsides in a dark corner. But at a movement from us he is up and off again.

I very much doubt then if the shearwaters in the room at night were behaving intelligently after all. Perhaps, unlike the puffin, they had met a situation beyond their power of grasping? Perhaps the shearwater is a stupid clod of a bird? Unable to move quickly on land, unable to rise in the air without a long preliminary run like that

Evening. Watching for the assembly of the shearwaters off the island coast

of a heavily loaded air-liner, has this bird, like the dung-beetle and scorpion of Fabre, evolved through the centuries a pattern of behaviour purely instinctive yet which, by the survival process, has made of it a nocturnal species while on land? Nocturnal because all the individuals which were foolish enough to appear above ground by day have been eviscerated by predatory gulls and hawks, and so have never perpetuated a diurnal-while-on-land race?

It looks like it at the moment. Instinct has done far more curious things. Survival and instinct, indeed, are great words to juggle with if you want to cover up your ignorance. But let us, at least so early in this book, avoid that nightmare word 'instinct.' Maybe shearwaters have always been nocturnal while on land, right back into the early days of their evolution? But how shall we know this? By the general behaviour of the whole genus, perhaps of the whole family of the *Procellariidae*, the petrels and shearwaters? Let us turn to the text-books again.

This is annoying. The skins of the birds are fully described and measured to the last feather, but 'habits unknown' is the label to most of them. Evidently these birds breed in inaccessible places where man has not been able to study them. Such information as I have been able to glean after a day's poring over monographs suggests that most species of shearwaters and petrels are strictly nocturnal, and that at the islands, the cliffs, and mountain tops where they breed they would be liable to attack by predators if they appeared above ground in the daylight. The few exceptions seem to be confined to the largest kinds, such as albatrosses, fulmar petrels, and great shearwaters, which are powerful enough to defend themselves against attacks. And so the nocturnal tradition has no survival value for these.

We have wandered far from the shearwater assembly, but the discussion has been useful. We have tentatively decided that the shearwater is nocturnal on land because it fears, with a hereditary fear, the attacks of predatory birds.

The explanation must suffice for the present, at least until a better one offers. Meanwhile we had better continue our sail through the assembly of Manx shearwaters to the north of the island.

We have watched the shearwaters swimming away, reluctant to rise from the smooth sea, their twin screws threshing the water with a beautiful easy motion. The tarsus is specially flattened for the purpose, presenting at each forward stroke a knife edge to the water, and so reducing resistance. The thin toes, joined by semi-transparent webbing, collapse like a closed umbrella at this forward impulse of the feet, but at the backward stroke they open wide to lever the bird forward.

As the boat rides down on the sluggish birds the nearer ones half-open their wings and dive. I eagerly lean forward to watch their progress in the translucent depth. No doubt they will screw along tolerably well with their feet? But not a bit of it. The feet are not used—they are invisible, doubtless lying parallel with the tail; they are most out of the way there. Instead, each bird simply *flies* through the water. They have turned their wings into the paddles of the penguin, and are beating the water with a forward hooking motion. But, most interesting of all, the wings are not properly spread so that each quill feather shows. In so dense a medium that would be difficult, would present too great an area of resistance for the strong but slender flexed wing muscles. There are no air currents to help here. No; the wing is opened only as far as the wrist or carpal joint; the 'fingers' with the primaries remain closed to make a strong solid fin or flipper with which to beat a way through the water. Each beat drives the bird forwards and downwards, so that progress is by a series of jerks with the tail as rudder. And though the bird is said to feed largely when hovering in the air just above the surface of the sea you can imagine that it is not difficult for it to find a breakfast of small fishes under the surface too.

Only a few have dived; the rest turn their heads to meet

the slight air from the north, and begin fluttering over the water. A slow-motion film would reveal fully what the eye can only just catch—the pounding of the surface of the water with the wing-tips, and the swift paddling with the feet. The birds run taxi-ing across the water, beating it noisily for some thirty yards before they are able to get safely away on the wing.

The movement is contagious. It spreads through the assembly; the clatter of wings and feet is like the roar of a mountain stream in flood. The magic carpet slowly rolls upward from the sunset-tinged sea.

Once on the wing the shearwater is all grace as it glides, careening from side to side, now skimming the water for fifty yards with one wing-tip, then rising to about ten feet above the surface, beating its wings once or twice or thrice to gather a fresh momentum, then skimming the sea for a similar distance with the other wing down.

There is here none of the swift simultaneous uprising and flight of other birds, such as notably the teal. Your shearwater will not be easily hurried. The flock has risen slowly, and from end to end has taken a whole minute to establish itself on the wing. Now it whirls around us in a great circle, a living wheel of which our red sail is the hub. A springe of teal would have dashed about us, simultaneously manœuvring at a speed that might deceive us into supposing that theirs is a flight synchronized by some mysterious form of thought transference. But if the leisurely shearwater assembly is but a slow-motion film of the flying teal, then we have the secret of so-called simultaneous flight-movement unravelled. It is after all only the old game of follow the leader. Those in front set the course and the long winding flock follows. I soon saw that some of the leaders dropped behind, or that more thrustful birds came forward and took up positions as pilots. In general the decision of the leading bird was followed by the rest, with exceptions to prove the rule—as when one bird ahead of the rest by several yards veered to the right, but those behind him led the flock in a glide to the left. Again, the assembly divided into several groups, and when we sailed back home it was then in three or four parts and, thus divided, had settled on the water again.

The flight of bird flocks has excited the curiosity of many observers. One author has said:

Their incredibly swift flight-movements are controlled by a mass-sensitiveness of visual perception, and drilled into a remarkable cohesion of flight-order by ages of immediate obedience to flock laws, with some element of physical or mental telepathy —probably of a sensitised physical nature, as yet not understood.

I asked my wife to read this explanation carefully aloud, and to tell me what it meant. My wife, who is a sensible woman, said the explanation seemed to lie in the first six and the last two words.

On another evening, with a fresh wind blowing from the south, we sailed again through the shearwater assembly. The sea was fairly rough and the broken water and the strong wind enabled the birds to rise from the surface without any taxi-ing. They were busily feeding on small crustacea floating near the surface, and to obtain these they were at times making short dives of two or three feet. Their sluggishness of the calm evenings was gone. They were lively and graceful, hovering at times like kestrels, and dipping and diving as kittiwakes do.

Later, like the kittiwakes, they feed in this hovering, dipping manner on the shoals of sand-eels and small fry which fill the inshore sea on the tides of summer.

CHAPTER III

EARLY SPRING

Now that we understand something of the Manx shear-water's movements on the sea let us haul the boat to its cranny in the island cliffs and begin where we left off on land—the arrival at the burrows in early spring.

We can go back to a February day when a new sheep dog, accidentally let loose at night, killed, among many rabbits, two shearwaters. I reproved the dog; and to turn the misfortune to account I sent the birds to Witherby. He reported them as both males, their sex organs much enlarged and ready for breeding.

Another night, while shooting rabbits by the light of a torch, I accidentally killed a shearwater which blundered into the line of fire as the trigger fell. This bird I opened myself, and found to be a female with a well-bulged oviduct and developing ova.

Here then was evidence to help my theory that the old adults, the most sexually developed birds, arrived first at the breeding ground. This, I thought to myself, is a natural and very understandable fact, and it is probably so in many animals subject to seasonal movements, from birds to such mammals as seals and mountain hares.

But my satisfaction with this theory soon suffered a blow. A few nights later, near the lighthouse on the island, I found two shearwaters which had been killed by striking a weather vane. (As a rule the red rays of Skokholm light-house do not fatally confuse birds at night, but occasionally in flying past they seem to be slightly confused and may then strike some part of the outbuildings.) I sent this pair to the long-suffering Witherby. He reported them both females in exactly the same state; ovaries undeveloped and small, ova no larger than a pin-head, and oviducts thin and straight. Evidently these birds had never bred, and were far from being ready then.

This was the night of 20th February, early enough in the year for few shearwaters to be about, and I had expected those few to be, possibly, all males in breeding condition, like the two I had sent to Witherby on 15th February. I had not forgotten the adult female caught in Dick's trap on 2nd February of an earlier year, but rather, in spite of this, since I had heard that the two on 15th February had been males, I had begun to think that the males might, as a general rule, arrive first, as they do in many species of migratory birds, e.g. wheatears and warblers. This theory had been in my mind because all the shearwaters seen at night at this early season had been sitting about outside their holes *singly*. Like the singing male chiff-chaff in possession of his wood the eager male shearwater (as I reckoned on seeing these single birds) had hastened to the burrow before the female, and was ardently waiting for a lady to come and approve his offer of heart and home.

Now, finding from Witherby that two of these early birds were females not in breeding condition proved my theory was quite wrong.

I turned my attention to these single birds. What were they doing then, male and female, sexually mature and immature, haphazard outside the nesting hole?

I watched as best I could, sitting near one bird and occasionally flashing a torch upon it. (I am obliged to call the shearwater 'it,' as the sexes are indistinguishable in the field.) I waited a long time in the darkness. It was cold. I lost patience. I walked about to warm myself, and after half an hour returned to the bird. It was still in the same position, facing the fresh north-west wind, sitting on the edge of the burrow and looking uneasily into the blinding glare of the torch. I promised it one more chance, and then I'd go to bed, for I was feeling ready for sleep by then.

When I returned in ten minutes I found the bird had anticipated me—it was fast asleep in the same position, but with its head turned back so that the bill rested partly under the scapulars, and the white breast feathers were slightly puffed out, their silky fringes overlapping the black of the closed wings. I smiled, but I did not wake the tired bird.

After all, coming to land for the first time after a long and stormy winter, the bird must be glad of an uninter- rupted sleep on firm unmoving ground.

Not all the shearwaters behaved so exasperatingly. One dived down the burrow, another taxied along and took off, but the majority stayed quite still, and, in the first nights of February, each bird was alone and silent.

Arrival, then, takes place on the first dark night in February. Perhaps one or two or at most a dozen make this first landing of the season. And for the rest of the dark nights of the month their numbers gradually increase from dozens to hundreds. By the end of March there are thousands present.

Calling begins a week or so after landing—the early February arrivals, as remarked before, being silent. On dark nights in March the calls increase in frequency until what we called 'bedlam' nights occur. The strange crow- ing noise may be heard occasionally during the day when one is walking over the burrows containing shearwaters. The excitement of the breeding season is too much for these resting individuals, and they give occasional whoops as if to express the state of their feelings.

Deep down in the winding burrows even strong daylight cannot penetrate, yet the hidden shearwater seems conscious enough of day. It seems to have an acute time sense. Perhaps in the day-time it may move along the labyrinth until, near the exit or entrance, a shaft of light warns it that the day and all its dangers still reign? I do not know. At any rate it is rare for a shearwater to appear above ground by day. When this happens the shearwater

C

generally rushes it, like someone dashing from one shelter to another in a thunderstorm. The bird scrambles out of the hole as fast as it can and taxies and flies straight to sea. There is rarely any of the puffin's slow and often fatal peeping and standing about in the doorway. Here at least the shearwater scores one point in seeming intelligence.

But apart from the corpses left by the gulls and that occasional crowing from underground, there is little evidence of the shearwater on land by day. Towards sunset the underground crowing is more frequent, and at dusk the volume of noise, though not yet continuous, has greatly increased. Then, about two hours after sunset, the first birds return from the sea, and, now that the initial silence of early February is over, they add their wild screams to the crescendo of noise from those birds which have been underground all day.

It is difficult to follow the nocturnal movements of the shearwaters. They arrive in what to man is darkness, and, preferring the black night, they are naturally not prepared to perform their business under the flood-light of the observer's torch. This must be used discreetly. How often, when with the shearwaters at night, have I not longed for the eyes of a cat or an owl! I was going to add, and best of all, the eyes of a shearwater; but my study of the bird has taught me to be cautious. The eye of the shearwater is surprisingly small, a little chocolate disk no larger than the head of a blue-bottle, or the head of Britannia on a penny. Such a small eye is obviously more adapted for making use of the brilliant light of the sun reflected from the surface of the sea, on and over which most of the shearwater's life is spent. While in the complete darkness of the shearwater's burrow the most sensitive eye in the world is not of much use. The bird in the burrow seems to manage very well by employing the other senses, those of touch, hearing, and, as it has nostrils, we can confidently add, smell.

But we are going too fast. We left the home-coming

shearwater in the air, flying over a great honeycomb of
rabbit burrows, in one of which, if it is a female bird, it
will presently lay an egg. That we know as a fact, but
whether, having laid the egg, the bird will incubate it or
leave this work to its mate, or perhaps even to another
shearwater, we do not know. Sea-birds, if you study
them long enough, reveal such unconventional habits
that it is not safe to assign to them any accepted pat-
terns of behaviour as laid down in text-books on birds.
And the Manx shearwater has never been studied in the
field.

Let us for a moment imagine ourselves to be a shearwater
flying in to Skokholm from the sea. We have had a long
day skimming the sea, feeding on small fishes and surface-
swimming crustacean life, and now we are anxious to be
home and busy about nesting affairs. As we cannot nest
in the sphere best known to us, the wind and the sea, we
have chosen the next thing, an island, which, surrounded
by wind and sea, yet has the necessary stable foundation of
rock and earth to burrow in. For centuries our forbears
have dug their holes in its surface, and like the ancestors
of man have, by their pioneering, made our lot easier.
We have in fact only to alight on the island to find a
ready-made hole.

But consider: the night is pitch dark, and below us there
is not one hole but a thousand, indeed a hundred thousand,
holes, a honeycomb which will not bear the weight of
human foot without the crust giving way. How shall we,
humans in birds' skins, discover our particular hole in
an acre of such flat and featureless ground? At least it
looks flat and featureless, this village city of the birds,
where all homes are alike and there are neither streets nor
directing notices. Here and there are outcrops of rock
from which we might take rough bearings, if we could see
them in the dark. These outcrops might help us to narrow
our search somewhat, but could not guide us accurately
to the chosen hole.

How does the bird find its burrow then? The question is really premature. We have not yet discovered whether the bird actually does know, find, and stick to the one hole in a season. All that is so far revealed is that the shearwaters arrive on the island about two hours after sunset. I can add here that I found that activity outdoors at night ceased at about two hours before sunrise. The shearwaters retired at the first hint of daylight; some went to the sea, the rest vanished under the ground.

Obviously, if more information was to be obtained, the life of the individual shearwater must be studied. To do this, some form of marking must be employed. And here the numbered aluminium leg-rings which Witherby sent me proved ideal. While for convenience sake I could start my study with the few pairs nesting in the knoll colony outside our back door.

Another advantage of the knoll colony was its comparative isolation. The view therefrom was restricted by the walls, roof, and windows of the house. (I may add that the shearwaters took no notice of a light which was often placed in the uncurtained kitchen window in the early part of the night.) The nearest shearwater colony to the knoll settlement was a few yards away, beyond a rocky buttress, but this was out of sight of my group, which I felt, therefore, to be a part quite distinct from the great shearwater rookery of the whole island, to the uproar and excitement of which the knoll added only a small quota of disturbance. Many such little groups as well as great villages were the natural result of the mixed terrain of rock and rock debris, earth and peat, and springs and pools which diversified the surface of the island. But a large group, with its labyrinthine and deep burrows, and its innumerable entrances and exits, would have been exceedingly difficult to study adequately.

I already knew that the shearwater was phlegmatic and uncomprehending of danger enough to allow me to pick it up as it sat quietly outside its burrow. It remained to

After the sun had set. The view the shearwaters had from their homes in the Knoll

devise some method of examining the nest in the burrow
without unduly disturbing the occupants.

The burrows could not go very deep because of the rock
on the knoll. I found that they ran only a few inches
along below the turf, and it was in fact impossible for me
to avoid treading through this flimsy ceiling occasionally
when walking there. When this happened I repaired the
damage by cutting a piece of turf from elsewhere and fitting

it over the breach. This gave me the idea of cutting out a
turf immediately over the nesting recess, which could
easily be found with the aid of a stick as a probe to trace
the windings of the burrow. When the stick could go no
farther that was the end—I had found the nesting recess.
I then cut a sod out in such a way that the edges fitted the
hole like the plug of a cask.

*   *   *   *   *

Occasionally in February the shearwaters came to the
knoll by the house at night, but not until the primroses and
lesser celandines were opened in South Haven in mid March

did they come there with any regularity. I have shown that the shearwaters followed no set rule in returning to the island; the old males and females might arrive first, or they might follow young birds which apparently had never bred before. And in later years I found the same thing in the village on the knoll—often there were young birds exploring there, without rings, in March, many nights before the old ringed adults returned.

As soon as they arrived the shearwaters began spring-cleaning. Singly or in pairs at night they attacked the soft, dry earth with their pickaxe bills, using their flat webbed feet as shovels to send the excavated material flying into the open. The burrows must be enlarged and the winter's havoc repaired. Every March morning, following a good dark night, I saw a quantity of the crumbling peaty earth of the knoll scattered outside the village homes.

We had at this time a fine Rhode Island cock, and a dozen hens to match, enjoying free range over the island. With the conservatism of the jungle fowl they never wandered far from home, however. The dry earth thrown out by the shearwaters made ideal dusting material. Jonathan and his harem rolled and wallowed in this every fine day. Their object was to indulge in the pleasant sensation of dry-cleaning their plumage; the result was the deposit in the earth of dirt, lice, feathers, and feather-scale. What became of the lice I do not know; I did not find them on the shearwaters, which are host to their own special parasites.[1] But on their part the shearwaters eagerly collected the loose chicken feathers and carried them in to line and to decorate their nesting recesses. In fact they seized for this purpose any small loose material lying near their holes, such as grass blades, blown twigs of dead bracken, even stray rabbit pellets. While bluebell bulbs and the roots of wild plants, obviously torn from the walls of the burrows, were also made use of.

[1] Lice: *Halipeurus diversus* (Kellogg) and *Trabeculus aviator* (Evans). Flea: *Ornithopsylla laetitiae* Roths.

Weeks before the egg was laid the nesting recess was fully furnished. But some birds were less particular than others, and might be quite content with a few blades of grass.

Even before Witherby's rings arrived I had begun marking individuals of the knoll colony, by smearing a little paint on the white underside of the wing. This marking was only temporary, but it gave me satisfaction immediately. On the second night a shearwater which I had thus marked in nest A (on the first night) came screaming out of the sky, and landed with a thump beside the entrance of the burrow. I flashed the torch and identified the bird. Here right away was evidence that the shearwater could fly direct from the sea to its chosen burrow. Of course the knoll with its outcropping rocks, and perhaps especially the whitewashed house beside it, were easy landmarks in the dim light, far easier than any which guide the shearwater, if guide they do, to its hole in the larger honeycombs of burrows.

I marked the inspection turves of the six burrows of the knoll colony with little pegs, numbering these from A to F. We can begin by following the fortunes of the shearwaters which frequented nest A.

CHAPTER IV

ADAM AND ADA

DURING April I watched eagerly for the appearance of the first egg in the knoll village. One bird or a pair was present almost every night in nest A, but no egg appeared during April. At last, in my eagerness, I lifted the turf twice a day; that is, if I found a bird there in the morning. I expected the egg at any moment, and I wanted to be sure which was the hen bird. Between the sexes there is no visible difference in size and plumage that I know of. Therefore, I argued, the bird found with the new-laid egg would be the hen.

On 6th May the nest was empty. On 7th May there was one bird sitting on a large, round, and very clean white egg. On the left leg of this bird I put a ring numbered AE 681. My wife, however, christened her Ada; and her husband who appeared on the next night, was called Adam, following the principle that the inhabitants of nest A should inherit names beginning with A, and those of nest B names beginning with B, and so on. Adam received a ring numbered AE 682 and an official-looking entry in our register; but it was easier to remember him as Adam.

If Ada was proud of her splendid pure-white egg, Adam was just as excited when he arrived to inspect it. At intervals during the day Ada had been giving out little cackles of—and why should I not say so?—joy. We could hear her muffled crooning through our kitchen window. Now as dusk came she grew more voluble. I went out and sat on the rocky knoll above nest A, and waited.

It had been a good day for birds. The day before had seen a sharp gale from south-east, followed by five hours of heavy rain, then a roaring wind from north-west, and

ending with a fresh south-wester. This rude boxing of
the compass had upset migrating birds. They had come
down on the island in their hundreds, bewildered and
weary. Swallows and willow-warblers had predominated,
but there had also been swifts, sand-martins, whinchats,
yellow wagtails, and a cuckoo. By the shore I had seen

A sketch map of the knoll village showing marked nests

common sandpipers, curlew, and whimbrel. A grass-
hopper-warbler, slender brown mouse-like thing, had crept
silently into the house. It had been literally weary unto
death. It had died in the hollow of my open palm.

Nothing of this weather would affect the shearwaters,
however. They preferred it as wild as possible. They
used the disturbed air as a lever to sustain their sharp flight.
Their narrow lines were built for speed, for the rushing
wind. Their fine wings could do little on land in calms.

To-night there was a fresh breeze left singing in the
wires of the flagstaff which crowned the little hill behind

me. The sky was clouded, and darkness came swiftly. Down by the well, at the foot of the meadow, a water-rail was calling with a sharp 'pip-pip-pip,' and then, as if angry at receiving no reply, it gave that wild strangled cry which is so exactly like the scream of a rabbit. In a day or two the sedge-warblers would return from Africa to the same thicket of hemlock dropwort by the well. There they would nest and the cock sedge-warbler would answer all the noises of the night with his more sweet, his polyglot notes. Indeed, since the shearwaters are calling all night, he would get little sleep. And besides that he warbles all day, too. The voice of spring is a bright song bubbling and dancing in the sedge-warbler's throat.

It was darker now. The scent of the bluebells came to me in a gust of wind. They are nearly perfect at this hour of May, leaping up in the recent rains, thick and strong of stem, sun and wind kissed, deep purple, heavy with bells, unlike your pale fragile attenuated woodland blooms. Here on the knoll they have adventured across the grass far from the bracken. As a rule they grow on the island chiefly in association with this fern which, springing up after the bluebells have flowered, provides the shade and moisture which the bulbs need for a full maturity.

Suddenly I heard the first cry of the shearwater on the wing, afar off on the edge of the wind. A wild cry, but softened by distance and lent enchantment by a new know-ledge of what it signified, a cry I was beginning to under-stand at last. Almost at once Ada, in the burrow close at my feet, answered. But no, it was not her mate Adam—it was too much to expect that of the ten thousand homing shearwaters Adam would be first.

The voice in the distance faded—the bird had turned away to the west of the island before the last screech. In the interval before the next I heard a whistling, a rippling note—whimbrel flying north to the Shetlands, the Faeroes, and Iceland. And then the gaggling of a skein of geese, a rare noise on this rocky western coast. I could hear the hiss of wings coming up from the south louder and louder, then slowly dying away north of me. But it was too dark to see anything—perhaps they were white-fronted geese bound for the ice-covered tundra of the far north.

Soon after 10 p.m. (by Greenwich mean time), with the whole island resounding with the wild screams of the shear-waters, Adam arrived with a piercing yell and crashed with a distinct thump upon the turf right in front of his burrow. He rested there for a second or so. Ada immediately squawked, saying as plainly as a shearwater may: 'Come inside, quick!' And Adam waddled in straight away. The light of my torch just caught his extremities—tail, legs, and wing-tips—as they vanished through the rather narrow entrance hole.

Now ensued a domestic scene which can only be imagined from the cooing and cackling that followed. I crept nearer the burrow and laid my ear to the ground above the nest-ing recess. The noise seemed to shake the burrow, and though it came up out of the earth as it were, it was quite unearthly. Similar meetings and greetings were going on in the other burrows, soft pedal to the wild night anthem of the island. I cannot describe even phonetically the individual notes of Adam and his wife. They were, I suppose, variations of the typical triple shout of the species. Yet it seemed to me that these variations had something of the intelligibility of spoken words. At one moment they seemed to be discussing the amazing new egg, at the next they were apparently billing and cooing, and probably, from the rising pitch of their excited duet, mating. There was movement as well as talk. But increasing intervals of quietude followed, punctuated briefly, perhaps, by an occa-sional sharp squeak. And from time to time the deafening duet.

This excessive connubialism was, I confess, wearing me out by midnight. The birds showed little signs of giving over. I wanted to see one of them leave, or perhaps both of them come out for an airing. They remained indoors, and did so, I felt sure, because it was their usual procedure, and not because I was outside. If I, motionless and silent outside, signified anything at all to these shearwaters in the knoll village it was, I believe, merely as a part, a harmless part, of the environment.

I should have liked to open up the burrow suddenly, so that I might have had a momentary glimpse of Adam and Ada at home. But I was afraid that, as I had looked so often in the day, a visit at such a crucial time might cause them to forsake the burrow.

I left them to it and went to bed.

On the following day Ada was incubating the egg. Adam had flown, but he was back to see his wife that night. The same meeting and greeting occurred, and Ada again resumed her incubation alone by day. It was clear, I thought, that the hen alone incubated. Perhaps Ada distrusted something—in that shallow skull of hers there seemed to be a feeling that something might happen if she left the egg for a single moment. . . .

This fear, I soon learnt, was justified. In other nests I found it not uncommon for the egg to be pirated by another shearwater, an outsider. Possession is nine-tenths of the law. Once the egg is between the legs of a shearwater, whether pirate or lawful owner, that bird can generally retain it against all comers.

Ada sat with the egg firmly wedged between and slightly behind her thighs. It fitted into a neat cavity or brood spot of bare skin there, which might only be discovered with difficulty when you had Ada in your hands—by ruffling the thick feathers the wrong way. This bare spot, only found in brooding adults, is present in most sea-birds, whose dense plumage is a necessary insulation to prevent the escape of body heat and the intrusion of water. The direct heat of the body is said to be essential to maintain a suitable incubation temperature. Gulls, laying three eggs, have three separate brood spots with which to accommodate their treasures. Guillemots have a single brood spot,

The entrance to Nest A in the Knoll colony

razorbills and puffins two. Gannets have none; they brood with their large webbed feet covering their single egg.

As Ada seemed a bit restless when I examined the nest on the third day, I decided to leave her alone for a while. I was curious, however, to learn whether Adam fed her at night. She could hardly sustain so long a fast, I thought. Adam himself did not seem to intend taking a turn at incubation.

On 15th May I could wait no longer. I lifted the sod of nest A. Adam (AE 682) was incubating. Ada was nowhere to be found, not even in the passage, which, to make sure, I probed with a stick. Moreover Ada did not appear that night, though I watched until my patience— for I had had a long day in the boat and with my sheep— wore out after midnight.

On the next evening Ada was again absent. I began to feel uneasy, fearing that she had been waylaid by a gull or lost in some disaster at sea. This fear was increased when she failed to appear on the next three evenings.

Meanwhile Adam continued to incubate alone. Every time I lifted him from the egg (in order to make sure of his identity by the number on his ring) I fancied he had lost weight. I am sorry now that I did not think of weighing him each day. However, this might have been the last straw, on top of his daily examination. He might have deserted. He was already more restless than I liked to see. He would try to scuttle off down the burrow when I opened the nest. I learned, therefore, to grab him quickly. He was more timid than his wife had been.

On the 20th Adam had gone, but to my great happiness Ada was back on the job. I detected a decided plumpness about her, almost a self-satisfied air. She had probably been doing herself well, out there in the sea, on her holiday among the little fishes of the ocean. Now she settled down to incubate. Often, gently lifting the sod, I found her asleep on the egg, her bill in the feathers of her back. The flood of light would waken her, and she would raise her head, turning it this way and that in alarm, and if I still watched her she would turn round uneasily, loath to leave but finally leaving the egg and shuffling off into the darkness of the passage.

I became expert at lifting the sod quickly, picking up the bird, reading its ring number, and dropping the bird back on to its egg, and then slipping the sod back into its place. Possibly the bird regarded this extraordinary interruption as part of an evil dream. I hoped Ada and Adam forgot my intrusion quickly and went to sleep again. I believe they did—there was very little movement to be heard after the sod was replaced—the egg was soon shuffled into the brood cavity, and incubation resumed.

Ada was five days on the egg this time. Adam then took over for three days, from 26th May to the 28th. Ada followed with three days in the nest, and then Adam carried on for four days to 4th June. This working of three to five days in shifts was an interesting discovery and something quite new in the practice of incubation. It was clear, too, that the sexes took a fairly equal share in the responsibility. And instead of the cock feeding the sitting hen, as is the case in so many species of birds, they arranged it more fairly: one was to fast while the other feasted, for so many days at a time. 'Adam,' said Ada, 'I am off for a week-end at sea.' 'Very well,' replied Adam, 'will it be a long or a short week-end, my dear?' 'Aha,' said Ada mysteriously, 'that all depends on the little fishes.' And off she would go.

Things were going on nicely now. I was delighted to find that the shearwaters remained faithful to the egg, despite my inquisitive peeping. It was now a waiting business, for me as well as for them. Nothing unusual happened in this period. I noticed a few more chicken feathers, dried grass, and a new bluebell bulb added to the nest. Adam and Ada were still a little house-proud.

For myself, in this month of May, there were a hundred things to be done out of doors. I had sheep to shear, a garden to tend, fish to catch, rabbits to hunt, and peat to cut. Let me confess that, on most nights, I should have been too tired to stay up for long with the shearwaters. Fortunately at this stage I did not have to. My main object was to find out the exact incubation period. I had therefore to be careful to disturb the sitting birds as little as possible. They were already becoming more timid. I feared that with a little extra attention they would desert altogether. So after 4th June I did not try to identify the sitting bird. I contented myself with one swift lifting of the sod and a gentle push of the bird with a stick. It was the egg I must see once each day until it hatched.

The birds suffered me patiently. Not for a day was the egg abandoned, or even uncovered. Adam and Ada proved an ideal pair, far more staunch to family ties than other pairs about which I shall presently write.

Hantzsch (quoted in the *Practical Handbook of British Birds*) gives one month as an estimate of the incubation period of the Manx shearwater. When Ada's egg showed no sign of hatching after four weeks we began to fear it was addled. And after five weeks—a period exceeding that for the incubation of the egg of the goose, the turkey, and the bustard—this fear greatly increased. Certainly the egg looked lifeless, if I may say so; it was no longer white—it was heavily smeared, and brown with dirt.

It was on the afternoon of the forty-second day of incubation that I found Adam and Ada in the nest together. I was surprised. What had brought them together so late in the period of incubation? It seemed almost as if they had remained with each other to discuss the unhatchable egg. But if we allow the shearwater no powers of discussion, what else had kept the pair at home? Had one of them been accidentally surprised by dawn and, so to speak, 'missed the bus,' missed the proper hour of exodus to the sea (one hour before dawn is the time of departure for those shearwaters going off duty)? And if so, why? Why should one of them have been surprised by the light on this particular day? What combination of circumstances caused this aberration? What, in plain language, caused Adam to stay at home with Ada on the forty-second day?

It is said that every little thing can be explained ultimately on physiological grounds—even it is said the changes wrought in the brain by meditation, by the art of the yogi. So be it. We have seen that the bird is a thrall to certain well-defined reactions as well as some less plain. But then, we may reflect, so are we. For the present, not to delve too deeply into the source, the secret of life itself, let us grant to Adam and Ada a pleasant share of that individual freedom which alone makes life tolerable to the human spirit.

On the fiftieth day our shearwaters had beaten all records for incubation that I, at least, had heard of. The white stork takes 30 days, the osprey 35 days, and the tame swan 38 days, usually less, to incubate its eggs. The golden eagle hatches in about 40 days, and even the vulture takes only 48 days. As for the largest bird in the world, I do not know the exact incubation period of the ostrich, but this flightless bird cannot be allowed to join in this competition; the female ostrich merely lays its eggs in the sand, leaving the male to guard them, and the sun to do most of the hatching, while the chicks when they emerge must fend for themselves.

Ada was on the egg on the fifty-first day. I had determined to test the egg by gently shaking it. If, as was pretty certain, it was addled, it would rattle. In that case it might be interesting to see how long the unlucky parents would continue their vain incubation. It was now too late to destroy the egg in the hope that another would be laid this season. It was 26th June, past midsummer. In other nests I had already tested the ability of the shearwater to lay again when the egg—fresh in these instances—is removed; and the hen had not laid again.

There was no need for any test with Ada's egg that

morning, however. To my delight it was pipped. A network of cracks half-circled the big end. I fancied that Ada looked more maternal that morning (I couldn't wait until the evening on these important days). Certainly she was anxious, and did not move readily from the egg when I slipped my hand into the nest. The chick called faintly from the egg and Ada, usually so silent when visited, gave a little half-strangled cry. And this is not sentiment on my part; the normal cry of the shearwater is a half-strangled shout. Ada, I repeat, gave a little half-strangled cry.

I pushed the egg under her and then put the sod back in place. The green turf of the knoll was soft as air to my dancing toes as I ran to the house to tell my wife.

Next morning we looked at the nest together. Ada—I suppose it was Ada, but we dared not wait to examine her ring—was brooding the chick, but it had only just emerged, a black ugly little ball wet from the shell. We hastily dropped the sod into place.

The egg had taken 52 days to hatch, and so had made a record for length of incubation of a fertile egg laid and brooded by a British wild bird.

On 28th June, two days after breaking the shell, the chick was dry and downy and as charming as—nay, more charming to us than—any domestic day-old chick. Not so active of course; indeed it seemed a weak little thing, with the eyelids barely opened and the head inclined to droop. It sat, somewhat unsteadily even so, on the full length of its legs. Its down was half an inch long and of a rich greyblue. This down had evidently been growing steadily during incubation.

The baby shearwater had a weak helpless little chirp, only accomplished with an effort that jerked the head and breast.

Half hidden and stunted in the rabbit-grazed turf outside the burrows, the minute blossoms of the lesser skullcap had opened. As if to celebrate the successful conclusion of the incubation period, Adam and Ada now began to

D

pluck, unmethodically and at random, these flowers and bring them inside, along with scraps of sorrel and grass. But much as I might like to fancy that this was done for aesthetic reasons, common sense requires me to believe that this decoration would never, in the complete darkness of the burrow, be seen by the shearwaters—that is, under normal conditions in an unopened, unwatched nest. Its purpose, whether understood or not understood by the parents, was to make the nest cosier and warmer for the new-born chick.

CHAPTER V

THE CHICK

ADAM and Ada shared the job of brooding their child during the day. It was defenceless enough to need constant guard at first. Once its splendid warm down was dry it needed little brooding, but they sat beside it and watched over it in turn for six days. If Adam was on duty for the day, Ada would be away at sea, gathering small fishes; and vice versa.

In the cliff-burrows of Skokholm the puffins had long hatched their sturdy black chicks, and all day were carrying sprats, sand-eels, and small fry to feed them. You could see exactly what was being delivered, for Mr and Mrs Puffin liked to stand about, holding the catch in the bill for a few moments before diving into the burrow to the insatiable chick, which ate the little fishes raw, straight from the sea. The feeble shearwater chick, however, could not cope with raw fish. So Adam and Ada swallowed everything as they caught it at sea. In their dilatable stomachs the fish was partly digested, the gizzard arresting and grinding up hard bones. The stomach juices softened the food until it became a semi-fluid pulp. In this state it was regurgitated and fed to the chick.

It was difficult to observe the exact process of feeding, but by degrees we pieced it together. The chick would become excited and start calling as it heard the parent entering the burrow. The adult, already loaded with the pre-pared food, responded immediately. The chick's feeble but ready beak would be scooped into the open mouth of the adult, there to attack and swallow part of the mass of food held in the parental gullet. The chick would swallow as much as it could hold for the moment, and withdraw. Both would then choke down what was left in their respective gullets.

Adam, or Ada, fresh from fishing at sea, was dangerous to handle at this stage of the evening. The loaded bird might at any moment disgorge the strong-smelling pulp, generally over your clothes, and the chick would have to miss its supper. This sudden disgorging was scarcely done as a form of protection or retaliation, though it had that effect. More likely it was done out of sheer fright. And it served several useful purposes, but especially that of lightening the bird for escape, for flight. So do kittiwake gulls and terns disgorge in alarm when attacked by pirate gulls and skuas. So do nesting gannets disgorge when approached by human intruders.

The chick—which for some inexplicable reason a relative of mine dubbed at sight, Hoofti—put on weight quickly. It had lost much of its first helplessness by the seventh day. It was alone for the first time in the burrow that day—4th July. It remained alone by day thereafter, except on the 7th, when Adam spent the day at home.

Adam was not brooding Hoofti when I examined the burrow on the 7th. He was sitting beside his child. Their heads were close together, as if they had been caressing each other; or possibly Adam had been spinning some yarn of the sea. It would be difficult to say; but one is entitled to one's fancies. Certainly Hoofti was taking an intelligent interest in his surroundings now. He could totter a few paces. His voice was sharper. Inquisitively he would nibble a feather or two, or a piece of grass from the nest-lining. And he distinguished you as an intruder; he pecked indignantly at your inquiring hand.

In the succeeding days Hoofti had much to learn, or at least to sort out of that packet of reflexes in his brain. Except during an hour or two at night he received no other assistance or intelligence from his parents. They merely arrived in the dark, stuffed him with the prepared food, and departed. This was all he was entitled to, all he required, for though he grew slowly he was decidedly healthy, and he was putting on fat steadily and keeping

Fursdon

Young shearwater, fifteen days old

The newly fledged shearwater; a queer mixture of down and feathers

almost as round as a ball. For the rest he had one fixed
code of behaviour: to peck and peck and peck.

Probably in the first place he pecked at his parent's bill
when hungry, as is the habit of nestling gulls, gannets, and
other sea-birds. But we should remember that this pecking took place in the utter darkness of the burrow. He
could (we believe) hear and feel, but Hoofti was pecking at
something he could not see, seeking as blindly as a new-
born babe for the source of nourishment. Even perhaps
he scented that nourishment—it certainly had a powerful
and fishy smell. And for many more weeks he was to
live in darkness, save for the unnatural occasions of my
periodical visits.

What precedent had he for pecking my hand when,
shattering his darkness with a spear of blinding light, I
opened up the nest? Hoofti, who, but for my intrusions
in their presence, would never have seen his parents at all,
saw my hand plainly with his grey, watery little eyes. And
he hit out at it courageously!

Well done, Hoofti!

So sat the young shearwater, with his back to the end
of the nesting recess, unseeing as a mole in the darkness,
but as ready to peck for his defence as he was for his food.
Hoofti, in common with other young shearwaters and
puffins, may often have been visited by night or by day
by inquisitive rabbits, rabbits seeking either shelter or a
place to nest. It was essential to keep these intruders off.
A very little scratching by a rabbit and Hoofti might have
been buried alive. Eggs have been buried by scratching
rabbits often. So here the everlasting pecking reaction
served well. Hoofti pecked vigorously from the moment
that Adam and Ada abandoned him by day.

The most remarkable feature of Hoofti's career during
the first month was the growth of his down. The first
or natal down grew for about two weeks until it was a
good inch long. Then a second crop began to sprout.
Shooting from the same follicles, this second growth

pushes out the first in the normal manner. But the first growth does not fall out; it remains attached to the tips of the second growth.

On 1st August, the 35th day of his life, Hoofti had down nearly two inches long. He had vanished beneath this astonishing screen. He was an enormous rich grey-blue powder puff. Only by searching could I find his legs beneath everything. To find his head it was necessary to steer my hand around the ball; when opposite his head my hand would be attacked by a sharp hooked bill suddenly thrust from shelter. His eye had somehow seen my hand, though I myself could not see his eye without a search, without parting the down hanging over it. For that reason it was almost impossible to photograph him at this stage— he merely showed as a soft blur on the grass.

Hoofti was excessively fat these days. He was doing well on one good meal every night, delivered in two instalments, one from Adam and one from Ada. We were very pleased with him, and as far as possible we now disturbed him very little. Days passed without an inspection. We ourselves were busy with the garden and the sheep, with our lobster and mackerel fishing, peat carrying, and adding the last touches to the rebuilt island house.

The young shearwater had seen very little or nothing of the fine summer which had passed over the knoll. Perhaps on the hottest days the air in his burrow had been somewhat oppressive. Crawling ants and beetles may have wandered in and out of the burrow in these hot days. His parents still occasionally brought in some green leaves of sheep's sorrel from the turf outside. I would like to be able to believe that they did it to amuse Hoofti; but in fact Adam and Ada were fond of toying with this plant, even before Hoofti was born, and I know that they ate it regularly—they sometimes threw it up from their gullets when I handled them. They now plucked other dwarf plants, components of the rabbit-grazed turf of the knoll: scorpion-grass, sea stork's-bill, pearlwort, tormentil, rock-spurrey, milkwort, eyebright, and chickweed; and carried them in to Hoofti.

But the dark blue acres of the island bluebells Hoofti had not seen, nor the magenta of the thrift covering the slopes of the island coast, nor, inland, the russet of the sorrel, the green of the bracken. Now, in August, the last foxgloves had dropped their fingers, were seeding about the knoll, giving place to the honey-coloured, honey-filled bells of the wood-sage. In the fields to the westwards heather was opening pink and white flowers.

Very likely, however, shearwaters are colour-blind. It is certain that Hoofti would never see flowers with a comprehending eye, for, coming upon them always at night in the future, they would be but as the variegated surface of the solid land to him.

Had it been possible Hoofti's eye would have been more taken up by the summer pageant of the island birds. Now these had flown. The guillemots and the razorbills had departed with their young from the cliff ledges. The puffins—in future Hoofti might regret the existence of puffins—had deserted their holes. Most of the gulls had flown, but enough were left to make life difficult when the time should come for Hoofti to go to the sea. Only the young petrels were left. On many a night Hoofti must have heard these harmless relatives of his squeaking from the crevices of our garden wall, and heard, too, earlier than this, the parent storm-petrel's love song, that strange cat-like purring. The petrels are the last of all the island birds to begin nesting.

I have said that we were inclined at this stage to leave Hoofti alone for days at a stretch, confident that Adam and Ada were feeding him regularly each night. This was a mistake. We should not only have looked at him, but we should also have weighed him each day. Had we known it his parents were now feeding him irregularly. And for this reason: while the August moon hung in the night sky, while its yellow face lighted the whole island, Adam and

Ada, in common with other shearwaters feeding young, did not visit the nest at all.

The same fear which prevented the adults landing during daylight prevented their landing during moonlight. That is to say, they were afraid of being attacked by predatory birds. In the days of Hoofti's childhood, however, I was not aware of this. I did not realize that the great black-backed gulls would hunt by moonlight. It was a vital point which I overlooked in my too hurried study of the shearwater that summer. It was a fact which afterwards solved one or two problems that had been worrying me, as, for instance, the unaccountable absence of one or other or both adults at night during the house-cleaning and the incubation periods. The moon, of course. How stupid not to have thought of it before! The moon, which regulated the movement of the sea, also regulated the habits of this sea-bird. The full moon coincided with the dark hours of summer night. Lunar periodicity—yes, a fine-sounding title—but, as we shall see presently, it was the *light* of the moon that mattered, and if the moon, no matter how full, was obscured by heavy clouds and rain, leaving the earth in darkness, then the shearwaters behaved accordingly and arrived to make their bedlam. But, I repeat, we did not know all this at the time.

We had now got over our surprise at the length of the fledging-period. Puffins, razorbills, and guillemots were away to sea at a month old or thereabouts, but Hoofti was still in swaddling down. Yet Hoofti, though all un-known to us he suffered fasts during the bright nights of August, continued to develop. His feathers were at last pushing up, under the great layer of down. On the 42nd day I noticed that the wing-quills and tail feathers were appearing from their sheaths. By the 50th day quite a lot of down had been shed. It formed, with the nest-lining beneath, a rampart around the bird, a little blue-grey wall. The white-feathered breast was now cleared of down, where it had rubbed on the ground. The nest was surprisingly clean, and had always been so, with scarcely a trace of excrement; this, I take it, because the food provided by Adam and Ada was predigested, and the hard fish bones and waste matter largely eliminated beforehand. The waste passed by Hoofti was chiefly liquid. He squirted it clear of the nest. It was absorbed by the soil of the peaty walls. By comparison the nest-burrow of the young puffin, a bird fed on whole raw fish, is a stinking midden.

On the 60th day Hoofti was completely feathered, with only a ruff of down picturesquely about his neck, his thighs, and his tail. He was still very fat, heavier in fact than his parents, and he had a really handsome shape and appearance now. His new suit of black and white was superb, as if it had just come from the tailor. In contrast his parents —last time I had seen them, ten days ago—were shabby; their coats had been faded and rusty, and the pink pigment in the legs, so fresh-looking in Hoofti, had quite vanished. Moreover they were silent now. We had heard scarcely any shearwaters screaming in this latter end of August.

And by the way, where were Adam and Ada? I had not seen them lately. True, I had not been out at night lately to catch them; but all the same the burrow somehow looked unvisited. There was a cobweb in the entrance on the morning of 27th August, the 61st day of Hoofti's life. Well, spiders spin their webs early in the morning, so this was no proof. Yet inside the burrow was a better clue: the rampart of nest-lining and moulted down which surrounded the chick was unbroken. It was only a little lower—and yet there too it was well built up and sprinkled with shed down—on the side facing the exit. If Hoofti had been visited and fed recently that rampart would have been disturbed, at least there would have been a breach made by the adults opposite the burrow passage.

It was high time something happened. Not content with breaking all incubation period records, Hoofti was now smashing the record for the longest fledging period. But he showed no emotion when I lifted the sod on the

62nd day. I could read nothing but complacency in the bulging white waistcoat and the eye, now grown as bright as a garnet.

We had by now placed an identification ring on Hoofti's leg. We hoped to meet him in the following years on the island.

That night I went out to wait for Adam and Ada. It had been a blustery day, inclined to wind and rain, and though it had fined off in the evening, it was not too starlit for shearwaters. I waited until after midnight. But there was no sign from burrow A. Two shearwaters had landed, silently (without a scream), opposite burrow C, in which was a nestling, a chick three weeks the junior of Hoofti. They had dived into burrow C and I could hear the usual feeding process going on: excited squeaks from the baby and a certain amount of muffled chortling from the adults.

I opened burrow A, thinking that perhaps Adam and Ada had slipped in unobserved. But Hoofti was still alone. I therefore placed a small clod of earth just inside the entrance to the burrow and in such a position that it would be pushed in by a bird seeking entrance, and out by a bird seeking egress. Such a small object would not deter a shearwater; I have known them to dig open a well-blocked hole in a single night.

I strolled over the island, visiting the great colonies of shearwaters a mile from the house, at the west end of the island. What was going on here in these important days? Perhaps I might get some clues as to the fledging procedure from this great shearwater slum?

Often in early summer I had been there at night. It was a favourite place to show wondering friends. You were impressed by the concerted roar of thousands of excited shearwaters on dark nights. You were even more impressed when a flying bird crashed into you occasionally. Your feet would break through the thin crust of earth, letting you down suddenly, throwing you forward on your knees and hands, when both these members were liable to continue your unexpected investigation of the underground homes.

The eight red beams revolving around the lighthouse on the westerly point threw a regular, a ruby glow over the burrows. It is interesting that the shearwaters, so sensitive to the white light of the sun, the moon, and the stars, ignored this red light entirely. The lighthouse had been commissioned in 1915; the shearwaters had been nesting at the West Head since time immemorial, and they had not allowed the strange phenomenon to disturb them. Perhaps its regularity and harmlessness were reassuring—for birds, like men, get used to many innovations that do not molest: scarecrows, trains, boats, aeroplanes.

In the breeding season the activities of the shearwaters at the Head were somewhat confusing. You stood there at night and listened to the uproar without being able to distinguish any individual performance, or to understand the comings and goings, the scratchings and thumpings and screams from above and below ground. You merely realized that here was a hive of birds enjoying the stimulation and protection of numbers, but from the sound of it having something of a fight to rear their posterity in such congested conditions.

That they were succeeding in this essential task was nevertheless suddenly made plain to me that late August evening. The colony was quieter now, only an occasional bird called overhead, or flashed through the rosy beams of the lighthouse lantern. Others were landing or leaving at various points in the honeycomb. But the hubbub of spring was over.

Suddenly my torch, and the glow from the lighthouse tower, showed me something quite new. A downy chick was sitting *outside* its burrow—in fact it was comfortably perched on a green hummock of thrift.

Astonished, I looked closer. No, it was not altogether downy. Beneath the tufts and ruffs of down it was well feathered. But it looked and probably was younger than Hoofti. It did not attempt to fly off. It gazed at the torch's eye with the same complacency shown by Hoofti.

Here and there, thinly scattered over the area, sitting quietly in the mouths of the burrows, or perched like this one on slight eminences, were other shearwaters, all of them youngsters and most of them conspicuous by their still retaining large amounts of down.

Were these nearly fledged chicks waiting outside the burrows, impatient to be fed by tardy parents? If not, what on earth were these adolescents doing, exposed like this at night?

As if in reply, one of them raised its wings high above its head. Aha, it was going to take off! It was ready for the sea, down or no down. I remembered that other birds —hawks, for instance, and finches—could leave the nest with a good deal of down still clinging to the feathers.

There was a gentle whirr of wings, and then nothing. The bird had not shifted from its seat. It had merely opened, exercised, and then closed its wings. It looked, I thought, exceptionally complacent about it too.

Its example was followed by others of these juveniles. Here and there wing-flapping went on for as long as I watched. There was some preening too, a good deal of it, and a rubbing of the beak and the head in the oil gland at the base of the tail and then an application of the result to the feathers of the body. This oiling action was to have its reward, as we shall presently see.

Most of these birds were fat, and heavy to lift. I found that the downiest ones, the youngest, were the fattest and therefore the heaviest. Those with only a little down at the back of the neck were not, I thought, any heavier than the adult. One, which I took for an adult at first, until I discovered a trace of down on the thighs, was very light indeed; it had lost weight perhaps because one or both of its parents had died—or, as I was at last beginning to realize, had deserted it.

The young shearwater ready to go to sea

*The young shearwater swims low in the water on reaching it for the
first time*

Yes, that was it—desertion. It seemed increasingly plain to me that these chicks had been deserted by their parents. Otherwise I should have seen some feeding going on outdoors under the ruby beams. I now began to consider that the adults that I had seen that night, which had all gone into or come out of holes without any sitting about either before or after, were feeding younger chicks underground. Those older nestlings above ground had, I considered, come out of their holes because no adults had visited them. They were hungry. No food had been delivered to them, perhaps for many nights. Now they would soon be making off for the sea, where they could get food on their own. I was anxious to see them make a start. No doubt they would get off in good time, before daylight caught them on land.

But these stout youngsters were in no hurry to be away. Half the night was still before them. They never even troubled to move out of the way of my exploring feet.

I pushed one youngster along with my foot, by way of encouragement. I gave it a good boost—not a kick, for I have too great a respect for my fellow creatures—a good lift by placing my foot partly under the bird and swinging it forwards and upwards. The young bird behaved like a clod of earth. It simply fell, solidly. True, its wings fluttered while it was in the air, but they did not sustain the bird, they served no purpose save perhaps to break its fall a little. The ground was fortunately soft; the bird merely bounced on a hummock of thrift. And there it stayed, as phlegmatic, as complacent as ever.

Surely that bird, in its present state, would never survive a scramble over the cliffs? Since it could not fly it must simply go to pieces, like the pat of butter it was, on the sharp sandstone rocks below the cliffs? Or what if that wad of fat and thick coat of new feathers served as a protective cushion, giving the bird resilience to meet any obstacle in its crashing progress to the sea?

Perhaps I had selected too young a specimen, one not yet

ready for the sea? Perhaps, in spite of their appearance above ground to-night, they did not all intend to make for the sea at once? I tried a few more, throwing them up in the air from my hands. They all flopped, badly, even the least downy juveniles.

The night was moving past. The cool wind had dropped now, making a flying take-off more difficult for a bird. But it was still very dark, with clouds hiding the stars over most of the sky. A migrating redshank called as it skirted the shore a hundred and fifty feet below. And thence came the sound of a light swell breaking on the rocks. The ruby beams flickered across the broken ground with monotonous regularity. I crouched against a tall outcrop of sandstone, in a good position to observe the birds by the artificial light. I might as well make a night of it now, and see what all these young shearwaters were going to do.

It was now nearly 2 a.m. I had my eye on six or seven young birds which I could just discern at their hummock posts each time the red beam flickered over the ground. From time to time I shone my torch on them. In the distance there was an occasional scramble and flutter, but vague in the darkness. My birds did not move for some time, except to exercise their wings.

It was cold, this waiting, and my teeth were chattering. Suddenly a shearwater—not one of my marked birds— came fluttering towards me, following the foot of the perpendicular rock against which I half lay, half crouched. It fluttered over my outstretched leg and passed on. The light of my torch arrested it for a moment. I saw that it had no down on it. This, and its rapid progress over the ground, made me realize it was an adult.

I switched off my torch and waited. Probably it was making for the sea. Just around the corner, not thirty yards away, were the cliffs. It would be able to tumble over them and be seized by the updraught. Then it would glide away to the sea—and to breakfast. Here, where I was, the rough ground and lack of wind made it hard for a bird to take off.

But to my surprise this adult had another plan, and a less laborious one, for getting away. It moved deliberately to a steep, almost sheer piece of rock near me, and at once walked up it, like a fly on a wall. Or almost—for the torch showed it was using legs, wings, and hooked bill, all three, to get to the top. In this primitive fashion, as progressed the extinct pterodactyl and as progresses the living hoatzin in Brazil, the shearwater gained the sharp ridge of the top in a few seconds, leaving me gaping in admiration below.

Then, with violently beating wings, it sprang into the air. It flew into the face of the slight northerly air—and therefore inland. It vanished at a smart pace in that direction. And no doubt, I thought, it would soon have gained enough momentum to start its beautiful characteristic swinging glide.

It had scarcely gone before another shearwater began climbing the rock in the same place. This other bird paused for a few seconds when it had gained the top, staying long enough for me to note, from the absence of down, that it was an adult. Then off it went, soon to be succeeded in turn by six more adults. Each went the same way, as to the manner born. When they had launched I examined the rock carefully.

There was quite a groove worn in the soft sandstone, a groove scratched clean of lichen and slightly smeared with dried dirt, the latter probably collected from the webbed feet of shearwaters, especially perhaps from the feet of those which in past springs had been underground incubating and feeding young in rainy weather. Their sharp toenails would naturally collect balls of dirt, which would be broken off on contact with the rock.

This groove was in the first place a natural fault or break in the rock. But it also showed signs of having been worn by the toes of thousands of shearwaters during the immemorial summers they had nested at the Head. It was obviously the well-known route to the rendezvous, to the high point for taking off. It was the road to the head-quarters of the local gliding club.

In other summers we were to watch many processions of adult shearwaters using this groove and the rock above, and many friends have since taken flashlight photographs of the birds climbing and taking off there.

No more birds came to the rock that night. I turned to the marked fledgelings. While I had been engaged with the gliding club three of these youngsters had disappeared unobserved. They had certainly not climbed the rock, or otherwise moved conspicuously about me, or I should have noticed them. The others had not moved. I con-centrated on these and was soon lucky enough to spot one moving. It dropped from its station on the hillock of thrift to a burrow entrance close beneath. My torch just caught the movement; and in another moment the bird had vanished below.

A second youngster soon did the same thing, and then a third.

These birds were not going to the sea after all. It seemed that they had only come out for an airing, and perhaps most important of all, to exercise their feeble wings. Now they were turning in for the day, under, as it seemed to me, the snug warm earth. For I myself was colder now; I was thinking with longing of my own bed.

Still, it had been an exciting night. I had made some discoveries, and begun to understand a little of the young birds' behaviour. I stamped around and beat some warmth into my numbed body, while the last fledgelings gradually disappeared.

It had grown lighter. The sky over the mainland in the east was more pale, while the shadows fled towards the dark blue of the western ocean. From their haunt in the boggy plateau in the centre of the island gulls began to call, coldly, mockingly.

I turned homewards, directly across the red sandstone

Duval

How the shearwater climbs the rocks

Salmon

A flashlight photograph of the shearwater
climbing rocks and taking flight from the top on
a windless night

ridges of the island to where, dimly to be seen as yet, the flagstaff marked the position of the house.

Passing through the bracken I disturbed several young shearwaters, some far from burrows. Evidently they had started for the sea but had not got far in their scramble. Now they appeared to be hiding for the day. Some were well covered in deep bracken, but a few were partly exposed, and one was sitting right in the open, inviting the attention of the first predator—gull or buzzard or raven.

These had already been at work. I passed a number of freshly eviscerated shearwaters. One victim was barely warm—it must have been killed by a gull in the night, for it was not gutted but appeared rather to have been mauled about as if the gull had seized it in the darkness and, unable to see clearly to do the butchering in accepted style, had punched and squeezed the life out of it, and then for some reason abandoned it. Possibly the shearwater, on its way to the sea, had even blundered upon a roosting gull, which had not been slow to make the most of the chance meeting. These young shearwaters, reared in the more centrally situated burrows, are much handicapped by having to travel a quarter of a mile to reach the sea. We have seen that they cannot fly and are obliged to cover the distance by scrambling along on all 'fives' (for we must include the useful bill).

Every autumn this exodus of young shearwaters to the sea attracts a large army of great and lesser black-backed gulls, buzzards, ravens, and crows. The island becomes littered with the skins of the slain shearwaters; and in October you can estimate at least six skins to each acre of the island, or roughly fifteen hundred in all; and this does not allow for large numbers carried to sea by the great gulls, which can tear their victims to pieces more easily in the water than on land. The great gull likes to drink with his meat, and, failing the sea, he souses his food in a pond or beside a rill on the island. It is in these wet situations on Skokholm that I find middens of emptied skins.

E

To return to that night of watching. As I passed over the knoll to the house, the eye of day was opening in the north-east. I glanced at Hoofti's burrow. The sod in the entrance was not moved. Hoofti had spent the night unvisited, alone, unmoving, fasting.

Hoofti remained unvisited, alone, unmoving, and fasting for six days and nights. This I knew from the fact that the sod in the entrance to his burrow was left untouched during this period.

On the sixth day, 3rd September, the sod had been pushed out—bodily. There was plenty of Hoofti's moulted down clinging as proof positive of his activity. He had at last burst out of his prison, driven by forces which he and his fellows had blindly obeyed generation upon generation. And what were those forces? Hunger, after six days' fast? Hunger seems an adequate reason, a compelling force. Yet though we may believe that hunger is the driving force, there is little proof. We must be careful.

If Hoofti had been merely hungry why did he not at once proceed to the sea and, in camp language, 'go and get it'— catch some fish for himself? Instead of this Hoofti only came out as far as the entrance of his burrow each succeeding night, and sat there, like the young shearwaters which I had watched at the Head. He sat there, waving his wings occasionally, and then at a decent hour, long before the east showed any sign of the new day, he retired below ground.

On 4th September I stayed the night with him to observe this behaviour. At 10.15 p.m. (G.M.T.) Hoofti came shuffling out of his burrow. He climbed the slight rise which lies in front of the hole (to gain a better position for wing exercise?), and then sat very quietly. The only noise he was responsible for was that of wing-flapping. No other shearwater visited him, though there were still a few adults visiting other burrows. He sat there, deserted —but I have no right to add, lonely. I do not know if he was lonely.

By 2 a.m. he had gone back to ground. I replaced the little sod in the burrow entrance.

Before retiring to bed myself each evening now I went out at about 11 p.m. to see if Hoofti was on the move. He was. He was out every night, sitting on his favourite mound. I thought he was unusually excited on the night of 6th September. He beat his wings more freely, and when I drew nearer to him to inquire into this matter, he suddenly took off and fluttered along the ground into a bunch of nettles about twenty feet away.

I marked the spot where he was hidden, intending to examine it early in the morning, and expecting he would perhaps have gone altogether then. Instead I was surprised to find Hoofti had found his way back to his burrow, and was asleep there in the morning. I smiled as I replaced the clod in the burrow entrance. Hoofti was showing some spirit at last, was awaking from his lethargic complacency. I fully expected he would take off on the next night, the night of the 7th. He was quite mature-looking now, without any down visible above the bright new feathers.

My expectation was correct. That night Hoofti pushed out the clod for the last time. On the morning of the 8th he had vanished.

He had broken all records with a fledging period of seventy-three days from the day of hatching to the day of departure.

(In referring to Hoofti it has been convenient to use the masculine gender, but of course it is not possible to tell the sex of the living shearwater until some incident of the breeding season betrays it. Therefore there is an equal chance that Hoofti was female. The truth might be learnt in some future season, if Hoofti ever returned to nest in the village where he was born.)

CHAPTER VI

It was a pity we did not, were unable to, follow Hoofti on his trek from the knoll to the sea. This, if he took the shortest course, was only a distance of about two hundred yards, and all downhill. Let us hope that he followed this route; no gulls roosted in this easterly direction, and predators were fewer and less bold near the house and the harbour during the day. If, however, Hoofti travelled north or west or south on leaving the knoll he had half a mile to cover, much of it over level or rising ground at first; and his chances of surviving to reach the sea would not be so good.

It would also have been interesting to watch his behaviour on reaching the sea. However, it is plain that we should have found it too dark to observe anything usefully on the water at night. The obvious way to secure this information was to experiment by putting young shearwaters into the sea in daylight.

With the intention of securing some youngsters for this experiment I spent another night wandering over the middle of the island. It was now the middle of September, and there was a noticeable difference in the behaviour of the young birds; although some were sitting about quietly, the majority were making their way to the sea.

What struck me particularly was that all the young shearwaters seemed to be heading for the sea by the nearest route. It had been calm for several days lately, and to-night there was not the slightest air to lighten their flapping wings; and this added to the young birds' difficulties. But they scrambled onwards, and, since all slopes on the island lead eventually to the sea, ever downwards. There is little

On Skokholm Pond. The gulls bathe in the morning after a night of feasting on helpless young shearwaters

doubt that this line of least resistance, the downward slope, was the determining factor in guiding the young bird to the sea—on a calm night. In such weather, as we have seen, the adults would climb a rock or some eminence so as to take off into space. I saw that the young birds avoided hills and eminences as far as possible, though not entirely. A few youngsters scrambled ahead of my torch uphill, and they seemed to do this not entirely because they were anxious to get clear of the advancing light—for I had my torch switched off more often than not—but as if they were purposely negotiating a small obstacle with the know-ledge that by so doing they were making the journey to the sea shorter. But the great majority simply skirted a hill, a boulder, an outcrop of rocks, rather than climb directly over the obstacle.

Where there were clean patches of rabbit-grazed turf the young bird got along fairly fast. It attained a kind of flying walk, pattering along the ground with the feet while sustaining the rest of its body in the air with rapidly beating wings. It could not keep this up for long, however, and every few yards it would stop to rest for several seconds, even a minute or two, before moving on. This apparent exhaustion is understandable—the bird had never flown or walked before—it was finding a combination of both processes pretty hard going.

Also the smallest unevenness of the ground upset this progress. Clumps of thrift and heather, stones, hedge walls and so on were typical stumbling-blocks. The youngster would bring up abruptly with its white breast hard against the object. Then, after a short rest, it would start again. If the obstacle were so low that the bird could raise its head and see over it, the bill would be reached out and hooked into the top of the obstacle, and then with wings spread the body would be lifted up while the webbed feet climbed beneath the body. The toe claws and the wings then held on while the bill got a grip farther ahead—and so the bird scrambled, not quite as efficiently but by the same means as the adult scrambled up the almost perpendicular rock-face.

Bracken was the worst obstruction. The young birds skirted it as much as possible, but some, coming from burrows within or surrounded by large patches of bracken, were obliged to force their way through it. They hooked and plunged along bravely, as if conscious of the need to get to the sea within the hours of darkness. I wished very much that I could have got some impression of what was going on in the young shearwater's head, as he struggled through the dense growth. On the level ground —and much of the bracken was growing on level ground —what guided the young bird out of the bracken towards the sea? Or was it mere chance that he forced himself free at all? With nothing to guide him (as it seems to us) did he go crashing about blindly?

The tall rods of the bracken were as the trees of a forest to the young shearwater. It was struggling as a man might struggle at night in a pathless wood. Somewhere was the sea, but on such a calm dark night and from far inland it would be difficult to hear the sea and impossible to see it. We know what happens if the bird fails to get to the sea before dawn; but does the bird itself know of the horrible fate awaiting it? I can only answer this question by using such ambiguous words as instinct, reflex action, inherited knowledge. It would be better to recite fully the facts as observed that night, and leave the reader to draw his own conclusions.

First of all the young shearwater moved exclusively by night. Born in darkness, reared in darkness, and abandoned in darkness, the youngster made its first move in darkness. Actually the light of a dark night must be as day to the young shearwater on first emerging from the blackness of its hole. At this stage of its life, being able to move more freely in its burrow, possibly it glimpsed the shafts of the true day thrust in at the entrance of the hole. But as yet those bright shafts were warning signs; it must

not be lured by them to make a day journey, no matter
how hungry it was or how inviting the roar of the distant
sea. Such a journey by day could only end in disaster at
the bill of some vigilant predator.

I can say, however, that I never found the young shearwater exploring the passages, nor found it anywhere by
day outside the nesting recess, except on two occasions.
I have twice seen a young shearwater emerge from a burrow
in full daylight and get away to sea without being attacked.
But in both cases the burrow was on the edge of the cliff,
and the bird had only a few yards to go before flapping
into space. It came out quickly, looked to left and right
(anxiously, I thought) for long enough for me to see traces
of down clinging to the nape, and then made a flying run
over the edge. A brave escape; and I should like to have
seen what happened at sea—perhaps a gull got it? I could
not follow the bird after it left the cliff. However, these
two incidents in ten years emphasize the rarity of the
exceptions to the rule. A shearwater attempting such an
escape in daylight from a more inland burrow would never
succeed in reaching the sea—unless a gale lifted its wings
immediately. We can safely say that any tendency of the
Manx shearwater to become diurnal while on land at
Skokholm is, very literally, destroyed at an early period.
(It is possible that a purely cliff-nesting race of Manx shearwaters, such as is found in the Faroes, might become more
diurnal while on land. But see Chapter XIV, pp. 166–7.)

We left the young shearwater struggling in the bracken
on a calm night. We speculated whether it knew its way
out to the sea, where the ground, being level, could not
guide it, and, the night being calm, no sound of the sea
could reach it. That night there was enough evidence for
me to believe that the young shearwater was thoroughly
handicapped by this lack of guides, and did not know what
it was doing. It seemed to be scrambling about aimlessly
in the forest of the bracken. The urge to move about was
there, but that was all. (There is a similar urge in the wings

of the migrating bird, an urge which bids it beat its wings at night during migration times, even when caged by man. On Heligoland I have seen this night restlessness of the migrant measured by means of an electrically sensitized perch, which recorded on a graph the exact periods and frequency of the bird's movements.) Some at least of these shearwaters had been scrambling about in the bracken, completely lost for several nights now, or so I believed. I picked a few up and found some of them very weak and thin. They had survived only because the thick bracken had hidden them from predators as well by day as by night.

One bird was quite emaciated, a mere bundle of feathers. I placed it in the open, on sloping ground. It immediately resumed the struggle, beating its wings violently and progressing downhill in short bursts. This slow and spasmodic progress was not likely to get it to the sea in time that night, which was already four-fifths gone, and the bird was still near the centre of the island. Moreover, after each effort, the poor bird collapsed upon its back, as if its sense of balance was destroyed. It lay there with wings outstretched as if dead. There was no cushion of fat on its bony breast as with other youngsters, and perhaps this lack helped to unbalance it.

At last it reached the edge of another area of bracken about one hundred yards from the sea, and, crashing into it, remained still, wedged between the stiff green rods. There I left it while I followed the fortunes of other youngsters. When the day broke I returned. The unhappy bird was still in the bracken. Its eye was dull. It died as I carried it to the house in a basket with other young shearwaters which I had collected.

The dead youngster weighed barely 10·25 ounces, or nearly one-third less than the average chick at desertion stage. Later, a series of weighings I made showed me that on the day of desertion by its parents the adolescent weighs about 15 ounces, and that after desertion it loses

weight at the rate of about 1½ ounces a week.   Youngsters
caught on the way to the sea weigh between 11 and 14
ounces.   (Adults weigh between 14 and 17 ounces.)

Before experimenting with the launching of the adolescent in daylight, I should describe our experience of watching these young birds on a windy night.   When I went out
one evening, with half a gale blowing from the west, I
found the adolescents behaving very differently.

Near the lighthouse, exposed to the full force of the
storm, the young shearwaters were all turned head to wind.
On my approach several got up into the wind and whirred
away.   A few were completely successful, rising slowly or
maintaining height sufficiently to clear the land altogether.
Others went quite a long way in the air before crashing;
and when I rushed up to these in order to follow their
movements in the torch's light they made off again, rising
and flying low with success for several yards again.   The
wind was sustaining them beautifully.   At this rate, I
thought, few young birds could fail to make the sea in
one night, even those inland.

I wandered inland, searching the bracken.   Yes, the
young birds were on the move there, and in general they
were moving to the west.   I threw myself down in the
fern to test the wind.   Could I feel any breeze down there
on the ground, below the fronds which rise about three feet
from the soil?   I could, just a little only.   I listened carefully.   What a rustling the wind made in the fern tops.
And yet, from the direction of the wind, above this noise
in the bracken, I could faintly hear the sea breaking on the
western shore, on the red pillars of Mad Bay.

As far as I could judge in the darkness, the young birds
in the bracken were all moving west.   They were, I thought,
guided by the wind—the wind which they longed to have
under their flapping wings; the wind which brought them
the rhythmic sound and the salt smell of the sea.

When these youngsters burst from cover at last they went
on into the wind, no matter if it led them by the bill up

or down a slope, or if at first it led them farther inland. They hooked and scrambled westwards steadily, madly thrashing their wings, which the wind filled and lifted, making possible little successful flights when they blundered from a small height, such as the top of a rock or hedge wall.

I tried encouraging them by throwing some as forcibly and as high as I could into the eye of the wind. The trick succeeded. Most of them whirred onwards and upwards into the gale, flying with strength and grace for as long as I could *hear* their wings (I could of course only follow them by sight with the torch for a few yards). Though they had never flown in their lives yet, the impetus I had given them had got them going beautifully. Comparatively few crashed in the distance, and these were the youngest, the chicks with the most fat and down. But when thrown *down wind*, the young bird behaved exactly as in a calm. It flopped heavily.

I walked along the leeward side—the east cliffs. Here was shelter from the west wind, almost a dead calm. Young shearwaters were behaving accordingly, following the slope, scrambling heavily, tumbling awkwardly down to the sea, crashing on the jagged rocks below.

From all this behaviour I began to believe that the young shearwater, when it comes out of its burrow, does not know what it is going to do next; even does not know that its next move will bring it to the sea. It is easy to imagine that it is hungry and discontented. But these first thoughts are dangerous. Its food supply, hitherto delivered in such generous consignments at night in the dark burrow, has been cut off. Nevertheless the darkness of the burrow is or should be associated with those warm heavy feeds of predigested fish. The outer world has hitherto offered nothing to the young bird. Eventually, it is true, the bird would die—as we have seen in one extreme case—if it did not reach its future source of food supply, the sea; but this does not prove that hunger started the youngster off from its burrow. It was obviously not hunger, but some deeper physiological change, that caused the parents to desert the young bird. These physiological changes in the condition of every living bird are associated, as in the case of man, with the secretions of the body-glands. Growth, adolescence, and maturity are the three great physiological periods of the bird's early life, and these are followed in after years by the three rhythmic periods of breeding, migration, and moult.

The study of glands is the province of laboratory research. We return to our province, the field. Whatever it is that drives the young shearwater from the burrow, the bird does not seem to behave intelligently. Rather it behaves—and we cannot easily avoid the horrid word—instinctively. Like the migrating bird—which in a sense it is—it simply obeys an impulse to travel, to keep going, to exercise violently every limb of its body. This results, on a calm night, in a spasmodic progress along the line of least resistance, that is to say, downhill to the sea; but many fail to get there. On nights when there is any wind the young bird travels instinctively into the breeze. Every flying-machine faces the wind in order to take off, in order to obtain the necessary lifting power. The wild bird does it instinctively. Wind sustains the young shearwater, and if it flies or scrambles long enough into the gale, it is bound eventually to reach the windward cliffs. Here, at the edge, the wind is at its strongest, and, as I have often seen, lifts the bird bodily upwards, giving leverage for a bold flight into the darkness over the sea. But on a calm night, those young birds which reach the cliff simply fall over it, when, if it is sheer, they have space to open out, to parachute, to glide, or to fly down to the sea. Where the cliff is shelving, however, they must crash from one ledge to another on calm nights. Fortunately the majority seem to damage themselves very little; at this age, when they start their initial flight, they have lost their excessive plumpness and helplessness, and have become thinner and tougher.

Probably, too, the thick new plumage covering the breast acts as a resilient cushion to soften these hard blows of accident.

*   *   *   *   *

We have spent long enough studying the young bird's movements between the burrow and the sea. We have collected a basket of these restless young shearwaters and put it in the house for the rest of the night. Now in the light of morning we release the birds from the landing-steps in the harbour.

Of course this experiment is not a true test of what happens naturally at night. There is bright sunlight on the water now. With the exception of a few thin ones which may have spent a day or two out in the bracken, these birds have not known daylight before. They have to face sunlight later; but, as we have seen, the night is the proper time for their first acquaintance with the sea.

First, we place one youngster on the edge of the steps, almost level with the water. It is a fairly stout bird, weighing nearly 15 ounces, and has a good deal of down clinging to it. Taken from the comparative darkness of the basket, it is decidedly uneasy. Without a glance at the water it turns round and starts shuffling towards the shadows at the back of the step on which it is placed.

'Too young,' says my wife compassionately, and I, too, am a bit conscience-stricken, though I reply in self-defence: 'But it was on the way to the sea when I picked it up, therefore it must be ready.'

Just as I am thinking I had better return it to the basket, the quiet sea breathes gently, throwing the edge of a wave over the step. The tide is rising. The wave licks up the nestling and swirls it into deep water.

Instantly the bird becomes alert. Raising its head up, it swims vigorously, wings half-spread and half-submerged on and under the surface. In this way it paddles rapidly, but with its feet only. It drives back towards the landing-steps, like a swimmer who has no confidence in himself.

'Much too young,' my wife reaffirms.

A wave lifts him back upon the steps and leaves him dry for a few seconds. Yes, perfectly dry, for we remark how swiftly the water runs off the oily plumage. That preening and oiling earlier now has its reward in a dry and warm swimming suit.

He rests there quietly for a moment. Then, instead of scrambling into the shadows again, he turns for a look at the sea. It wasn't so bad after all, he seems to be thinking; by Jove, it was easier going than this hard land—and so refreshing, too! But when the next wave comes upon him, he scrambles to escape it. It's rather frightening, this mighty sea!

The wave comes back to claim him, however, and in spite of his desperate hooking and reaching with bill, legs, and wings, it sweeps him back into deep water. But he is obviously not so alarmed this time—not now that he has got his second sea-legs. He swims out into the open water, and he moves less frantically.

Suddenly he dips his bill and holds it up. He is swallowing water, the first water he has ever tasted. Salt water, of course; but why not? The shearwater, like most other marine birds, will drink nothing else in his life. We, who are so accustomed to drinking fresh water, fancy that salt water will be harmful to other warm-blooded creatures. This youngster, on the contrary, is delighted with its sharp taste. He goes on dipping and sipping, for a moment seeming to desire nothing but to quench a big thirst, a ten weeks' thirst!

Idly I wonder whether thirst is not a factor in calling the young shearwater to the sea?

The sea is becoming a place of delightful sensations for the young bird. Ignoring us, he now starts a vigorous bath, emulating all the movements of the farmyard duck, plunging his head under, throwing the water over his back, and shaking his wings and puffing out his feathers to achieve a cooling penetration.

We are delighted to see him, who was so unaccountably deserted, now so happy. I smile significantly at my wife. We did the right thing in bringing him to the sea.

In that moment of turning my head the young bird vanished completely. I am astonished until my wife shouts excitedly: 'He has dived! Time him, time him!'

He is under the water for long enough for me to fear that he is drowned. The seconds move slowly. Actually he is under for only twenty seconds. He reappears like a cork, bobbing up a few yards from where he dived. One swift look round and down he goes again. He is revelling in this new sensation, this unexpected new power. He thrusts with both legs and wings, submerging quietly with a swift dip of the head. We can watch him for some distance through the clear water. Like the adult, he is swimming with his half-opened wings only—once he is below the surface; his paddles are then flattened back against his tail, to share with that member the duty of rudder. His black back and wings merge into the dark brown leaves of the laminaria on the floor of the harbour.

Down there, too, close against the landing steps, we see shoals of sand-eels and the three- and two-inch fry of mackerel, herring, and pollack. They are darting this way and that in greenish columns, moving with the simultaneousness, the regimentation, of flocked birds. Riches indeed for the hungry shearwater, who will soon have the pleasure of swimming through dense masses of these young fishes which, hatched in the spring, now fill the in-shore waters in late summer.

The food problem will no longer trouble our fledgeling. Indeed, we would not be surprised to see him, after this second dive of his, rise with fish. But he does not—at least there is nothing in his bill—and probably he is still enjoying the sensation of diving and exploring in this new medium where he moves so easily, so dreamily. He comes up only for air now—seventeen seconds below, six seconds on the surface, and then down again (his third dive) for twenty-two seconds. Nor does he come up gasping for breath, half-choked with water in his windpipe; he is born a diver; his epiglottis closes automatically under water.

Each time he comes up he is farther away now. He is swimming confidently, both above and under water, striking away from the shore. He has finished, is probably only too glad to be finished, with the land and its unpleasant associations of thirst and hunger and lurking attack. Without another look at the island he forges on, making quite a bow-wave at his white breast. Then under he goes and out of sight again. When he comes up for the sixth time, he is half lost in the silver light on the distant sea, beyond the outer rock of the harbour.

We now take the heaviest and fattest nestling, which has also a lot of down on his head, thighs, and tail.

'A little young?' comments my wife.

'Not a bit; you see how well that first bird took to the water,' I advise her. 'Well, this one is fatter and oilier, and should do even better.'

I placed Number Two on the step.

The increasing wave has him at once, sweeping him well out into the pool of the harbour. Just as alarmed as Number One, he swims rapidly, this time across to the opposite rocks. There he scrambles up the shelving sandstone on all fives. But he next does the unexpected. Up he goes, up and up, until he is twenty feet above the water. He works along until he comes to a crack, a cul-de-sac. There, in shadow, he crouches. He remains there unmoving, until we grow impatient. It seems he does not propose to move again. Perhaps he intends waiting for darkness? Certainly he seems to object to giving a performance in daylight. I begin to think that my wife is right, that he was picked up too young. His 'look' is not yet fully to the sea. Possibly he would have gone back to earth last night if I had not picked him up.

As we cannot easily retrieve him from that niche in the rocks, I try a third bird, a rather thinner one with scarcely any down left, and weighing twelve ounces. (We weighed and ringed all these fledgelings.) We should, I think, try throwing this one into the sea—as if he were tumbling into it naturally. I go to the top of the landing steps and drop him fifteen feet to the sea.

My imagination allows me to suppose that there is a surprised look on the bird's face as he splashes the water. Anyway he only paddles a few strokes with wings half-spread on the surface before diving. He does not bother to drink or wash. After thirteen seconds he rises a few yards away. He begins to swim vigorously for the open sea. I note how low he carries himself, only the head and neck and a little of the back above water. He soon dives and remains under for sixteen seconds. He rises this time still farther from the landing steps. He continues diving and swimming at the surface alternately as he moves off. At the harbour entrance a great gull suddenly swoops down upon him. But he avoids this dangerous contact by diving. At once the gull flies away, as if aware that the attack is not worth pressing. And very soon the sunlight on the water obliterates the young bird for us.

The fourth fledgeling is stout and weighs fifteen ounces. I place him on a high step and encourage him with a gentle push. He flutters down at an angle of about 45 degrees. He varies the behaviour by thrashing the water with his wings as well as his paddles, as if he were moving along solid ground, though actually, as his wings are submerged and heavy with water, he is not able to extend and beat them properly. Rather he uses at the surface that hooking movement of the half-closed wings with which he will presently swim under water. But he soon gives up this unprofitable churning and begins quietly to sip water. Then he washes in the manner of Number One. He concludes the exhibition with a long dive of twenty-four seconds' duration.

Coming up close to the shore where Number Two landed, he, too, makes a half-hearted attempt to land. Foiled by the backwash of a wave he gives up the attempt (gladly, I thought), and resumes his ablutions. Suddenly he makes his second dive, a matter of twenty-one seconds, coming up well away from the rocks. Then, following Numbers One and Three, he alternately swims and dives until he passes out of sight seawards.

This, we found in the trials carried out on other fledgeling shearwaters, was the typical behaviour of all individuals that were in sound health. Timed dives varied between five and thirty, and averaged twelve, seconds. It remains only to add a note on the behaviour of some emaciated youngsters.

One bird, for instance, recovered from a bracken area, was extremely light, rather less than ten ounces in weight. It had evidently suffered an unusually long fast since desertion. Its eyes were sunken, with a white froth in the corners. Its legs appeared strong, but instead of sitting on the breast in the normal way, it was inclined to roll over on one side or the other. But I hoped the sea would remedy these distresses.

I placed it in the water of the harbour. It floated off very lightly, much higher in the water than the others. It beat the water only with its half-closed wings, making little progress. It was then I realized that it had lost the use of its legs. These were stretched backwards and up in the air over its back in a strange manner. The webs appeared over its back, like the curly feathers of a drake's tail. And there they stayed.

I was astonished at this rigidity, this curious mizen-sail effect. But it was plain that the bird was altogether abnormal. It did not, probably could not, dive. It hunched along with half-submerged wings, working away to sea before a slight off-shore breeze. It made no attempt to get under water, or to drink or wash.

Outside the harbour it was quickly spotted by a great

F

gull. The predator swerved and immediately parachuted down to the water beside the shearwater. Even so the shearwater took no notice, but continued to flap spasmodically. I thought that perhaps, in addition to its other miseries, it was blind. The gull swam closer, suddenly dealt the bird a savage blow on the head, then proceeded to worry, drown, and eviscerate the unlucky youngster.

Other thin and half-blind fledgelings which we have found on the island and taken to the sea have behaved in the same way, especially with regard to the curious rigidity and attitude of the legs. And they have always been killed by gulls before they have had time to get far at sea. In view of this we made it a rule to release all such sickly birds at night, so as to give them a better chance to recover in the darkness at sea. But it is doubtful if many of these recover. It is more likely that by not getting to sea at the psychological moment these birds outwear their physiological preparedness, and will merely pay at sea the same penalty—death at the bill of the first predator—as that from which we have saved them on land.

*　　　*　　　*　　　*　　　*

If we could have followed Hoofti and his fellow fledgelings out to sea that autumn we should have been glad. We were very curious to see how they behaved at sea, and where they migrated to. But it was impossible to sail far from the land in our small boat.

Now and again, in September and October, in sailing about the island and when making crossings to other islands and to the mainland, we passed a solitary shearwater. We would point to it and pretend it was Hoofti. But this was a more than ten-thousand-to-one chance. Ten thousand or so young shearwaters are launched from the islands of Skokholm and Skomer each autumn. The surprising fact was that we saw so little of them. Only in the mornings as a rule were these solitaries to be seen at sea near the island—any shearwater seen near the island early in the day was likely not to be an adult, for the adults do not haunt the immediate vicinity of the island until the evening; they are off at sea fishing then, and most likely at this season deep in moult, with no thought of children left at home. Moreover these solitary young birds are recognizable by their spruce and fresh appearance, adults being now worn and brown-looking; and, finally, they never take to the air to get out of the way of the boat. They have not yet learnt to fly in the air. They escape by diving and flying under water.

But although these young birds seen near the islands had only just been launched and had not had time to get far, they were already making strong efforts to leave the land behind, to get as far as possible to sea. Now and then we saw a great black-backed gull swoop at one of these youngsters swimming at the surface, but seldom with success. As we have seen, the young shearwater, unless stupefied by long starvation on land (and I remember having to shout at and warn off one gull which alighted beside one young shearwater at sea), merely dived deep and swam a long way under water before reappearing. Gulls can make only the shallowest of dives.

These attacks may help to drive the young shearwater into the ocean where these gulls are absent, or at least scarce. What other dangers await the fledgeling in the open Atlantic we do not know. We might, however, learn a little of the bird's movements at sea by ringing large numbers of youngsters.

This extensive ringing I had already begun. I intended to ring as many as possible in future years.

CHAPTER VII

IN OTHER HOMES

Up to the time of deserting Hoofti, Adam and Ada had been a model pair. Their household in the peaty turf had witnessed an ideal sharing of the parental duties of incubation and of feeding the chick. And earlier than this, their love-making had been an idyll. There might be ten thousand shearwaters on the island, but as far as the household of Burrow A was concerned, there were only two—Adam and Ada. Not one of the remaining nine thousand nine hundred and ninety-eight intruded in the affairs and the domesticity of Burrow A, not even, it seemed, to pay a neighbourly call.

Yet this example was lost upon the rest of the shearwaters in and near the village on the knoll. Scandalous events took place in homes only a few feet from Burrow A. We shall relate these things in their order, starting with the affairs of the summer of 1929 in Burrow B.

This was a substantial home, a desirable residence with a winding burrow about six feet long. On 7th May a pair of shearwaters was sitting in the end recess. There were some slight furnishings of dried grass and the leaves of wood-sage. Everything was ready for the egg. On the 8th the burrow was empty.

On the 9th there was a single bird—subsequently to be known as Bill—which I ringed. This bird paid visits, still alone, on the 11th and 14th. On the 17th there appeared a new bird, which I ringed AE 689. AE 689 was always a ghost-like figure in the village, or perhaps, more aptly, a ship gliding by in the night. He looked in at this nest for three years in succession, as if he was, all the time, seeking a lost mate. It became a duty call. It

was not until 1931 that I found him with a mate, settled
in a hole just outside the knoll with a new (unringed) bird.
And there his brief tale ends.

Meanwhile in nest B a third bird appeared on 18th May
(1929). She was alone and had just laid an egg. Ringing
soon proved that she was Bill's mate Bess. She was a
shy bird and on the 19th, when I lifted the sod, she left
the egg. She vanished that night, leaving the egg to a
fourth bird, AE 700, who was sitting tightly on it next
day!

At first I thought this was a case of two pairs using the
same nest, but in the light of later events I cannot now be
certain. AE 700 disappeared and I did not meet him again
until next year. Then, like AE 689, he poked his bill
into this same nest, only to vanish immediately and for ever.

From 20th May onwards Bill and Bess were uninterrupted
by any other shearwater. But incubation was not allowed
to proceed smoothly. Burrow B was too desirable a
residence. Rabbits constantly visited it, and, in spite of
hideous vocal protest, emphasized by the angry bills of the
birds, the rodents began digging a new gallery, apparently
determined, since the birds would not allow them to share
one recess, to divide the burrow into two parts. The damp
excavated earth was skilfully showered into the old recess
on top of the incubating Bill or Bess alike. The egg
became filthy, and was twice completely buried for a day
or two. I helped the shearwaters to recover their essential
property, but it had suffered too many hardships ever to
hatch. On 6th July Bess was still sitting on a cracked
and rotten egg.

In the following March (1930) Bill and Bess came back
to the burrow. The rabbits had finished digging the new
wing, and, with the characteristic inconsequence of their
race, had entirely deserted the burrow. This left two
desirable recesses with one entrance hole. As it happened,
I was so busy that year that I did not trouble to open up
the new wing with an observation sod. But what went on

in the old nest was sufficiently promiscuous to keep me occupied making notes. Last year's intruder, AE 700, constantly put in an appearance. There were also other visitors, notably AE 701, a bird which sometimes sat side by side in the nest with Bill; on these occasions there was no quarrelling, so perhaps AE 701 was female. One night late in March Bill was at home with this bird and a lot of cackling was going on when AE 700 came crashing out of the sky, to land with a thump on the ground near the burrow entrance. On a night in May, AE 684 (from nest D, in 1929) shared the burrow with the interloper AE 689, and AE 701 lurked in the passage, growling to himself about something.

Bill and Bess, however, retained essential possession in spite of these intrusions, and once they had really settled down to incubate, the others gave up visiting the burrow. This second year Bill and Bess had better fortune and reared their chick successfully.

*   *   *   *   *

In Burrow C there were at first in 1929 two pairs, but as soon as Carol and Caroline had produced their egg on 26th May the other pair vanished. This nest was in a burrow about four feet long and was nicely lined with dried grass collected from outside, and with roots plucked from inside the burrow.

Carol and Caroline followed the plan of incubation adopted by Adam and Ada, who had, that year, three weeks' start over them. They incubated in shifts: Caroline, for instance, on 28th and 29th May, and on 1st, 4th, and 5th June, and in between these days Carol sat on the egg. On 14th June the pair were on the nest all day, anticipating by four days a similar 'at home' by Adam and Ada, who, you will remember, spent 18th June with the egg.

After 5th June I did no more than glance once a day at the egg under the brooding adult, lifting and replacing the sod quickly. I did not want the birds to desert.

At last, on 17th July, I heard the chick squeaking faintly in the egg—which Caroline was brooding. The shell was not cracked until next day. On the 19th the chick had just emerged and was not yet dry. It had taken 54 days to hatch.

For five days Toofti (as this chick was relentlessly called by my young sister) was warmly covered by one of the adults. On the sixth day it was alone, but on the seventh and eighth days Carol brooded his child. After this Toofti remained alone by day.

There was no need for me to visit Toofti more than every other day during his downy days, for he grew just as slowly and as surely as his senior in nest A, Hoofti. His feathers were well grown on the 50th day, 7th September. On the 15th he weighed 13½ ounces. A week later I watched at the entrance of his burrow until midnight, but no adult came near. I placed a small clod in the mouth of this burrow, poising it so that it would roll in or out at the first touch. The clod had not been moved by the morning, but by the second morning, 16th September, it had rolled *down inside* the passage. There was no down clinging to it or to the walls of the passage. Was this a last and tardy visit by Carol or Caroline or both—a last visit with the last feed of warm salivated fish for the maturing Toofti?

From the 17th to the 22nd Toofti moved not from his nest, and none visited him. On the 22nd, after six days' fast, he weighed 12½ ounces. On the night of the 23rd he pushed his way out for the first time, knocking the sod forwards and leaving a trail of down thence to the slight mound in front of the burrow—that mound, now grass-grown, which was, in spring times, thrown up by the adults excavating within the burrow. I returned the sod next morning. Toofti thrust it forth every night up to the 29th, when, on looking at the nest, I found he had gone.

Toofti had lived 72 days in his burrow, after 54 days

developing in the egg; in all 126 days. Hoofti's times, as we have seen, had been 73 days as a chick after 52 days in the egg; in all 125 days.

*   *   *   *   *

Nest D was outside the knoll in a short burrow about 3½ feet long. It was lined with dried grass and dead bracken stalks about 3 inches long. When I opened it on 15th May I found one bird brooding a slightly incubated egg. This bird I ringed AE 684. I removed the egg, feeling sure that another would be laid to provide me with a true record of the incubation period. AE 684 and AE 692 frequented the nest on most nights thereafter and occasionally by day up to 22nd June. After that they deserted the burrow. A second egg was not laid.

*   *   *   *   *

Nest E was constructed at the end of a burrow 8 feet long. It was lined with dried grass. On 27th April it contained a bird on a slightly incubated egg. I removed the egg as in nest D and for the same reason. The pair, AE 686 and AE 691, visited the nest at intervals up to 1st July, but no second egg appeared. Rabbits had been in and out of the burrow since this pair of shearwaters began to lose interest in the nest during June. In the middle of July a doe built a nest of grass and fur and littered there without molestation.

*   *   *   *   *

Nest F was (for this year) outside the knoll colony, in a very short burrow under a clump of heather. I could reach its recess by thrusting my arm through the entrance. There was thus no need for an inspection lid above the nest. In 1928, while I had been so busy rebuilding the island home, I had spent comforting moments watching a young bird grow up in this nest, though I had not had time to make any regular observations. He had been dragged out occasionally to show to curious visitors.

In 1929 this nest was early lined with fresh stems of heather, taken from the clump around the hole. This activity was of course accomplished at night; but as this burrow was far from the house I seldom visited it then. Meanwhile no birds stayed there over the day until 16th May when I found Freda sitting on her new-laid egg. She continued to incubate for two days, then disappeared for four days. Fred did not take his turn; indeed he was as yet only a name in waiting, though in these four nights he may have visited the nest—I could see fresh excreta splashed at the entrance to the burrow. Freda returned to duty on 24th, 26th, and 29th May, and on 5th June. At this rate, of course, the egg could not be expected to hatch. On 2nd June a second bird at last appeared and incubated the egg for twenty-four hours, thus earning a ring and the name of Fred. But he may not have been the genuine husband of Freda; he may have been an adventurer, male or female, like some of the casuals in the other nests. Freda herself gave up the unequal struggle in a month, and deserted the egg after one final day of brooding it on 14th June.

Possibly the shortness of the burrow (quite a strong light must have reached the sitting bird), added to my inquisitive peeping and handling, had something to do with this desertion. I do not know.

*   *   *   *   *

Nest G presented yet another facet of shearwater life. The burrow was about 5 feet long, and the recess was lined with 15 dead bracken stalks, each not above 4 inches long (which is a convenient length for carrying broadside in the narrow burrow). Two birds frequented this burrow, a perfectly desirable residence, and yet I found no egg here in the whole of that spring of 1929. Perhaps the hen was immature or barren? But I think it more probable that she had accidentally dropped her egg elsewhere (even at sea?). In later years there were mature females in the knoll village, known to me over years, which occasionally failed to lay an egg in their chosen nest—I feel inclined to believe that these had lost their eggs elsewhere. And we have seen that a shearwater does not lay a second egg in the same summer.

* * * * *

Outside the knoll, in a stony burrow near the flagstaff, a puffin had contested the site with a shearwater. The puffin, after several pitched battles, had taken over the shearwater's egg, incubated it, but failed to hatch it.

In later years I sometimes found a puffin fighting with a shearwater in the passage of, or outside, a burrow. But on the whole such disputes were rare. Each species kept principally to its special terrain: the puffin to the burrows in or near the cliffs, the shearwater to the more inland burrows. There were exceptions: as, for instance, the shearwaters completely monopolized the cliff burrows at the Head; and odd pairs of puffins nested inland near the house.

In combat they were both good fighters. The puffin was perhaps more formidable, with its powerful axe-like parrot bill.

CHAPTER VIII

THE SUCCEEDING YEARS

In 1930, soon after the leaves of the lords and ladies had unrolled in South Haven and the blades of the vernal squill had pierced the wet ground, the first shearwaters returned to the island. The date was 13th February. They were numerous by the 26th.

We were delighted to find that Adam and Ada had returned to Burrow A. They visited their old nest fairly regularly at night in March. Their leg rings had worn thinner in their six months at sea, but the inscriptions were very legible, and I did not then think of giving them new rings. This, as we were to realize in the third year, was a mistake. We should have changed the rings of all the inhabitants of the knoll colony each spring. Experience was to teach us that these thin aluminium bands did not always last two years; they became so eaten by the weather and the salt as to drop off at any time after a year. And in this way, though we were lucky in preserving the identity of Adam and Ada for many a year to come, we lost contact with some other important individuals of the knoll village.

Adam and Ada cleaned out the burrow on March nights and began lining the nest. They ripped some large bluebell bulbs from the walls of the passage which they had been scraping, and they used these bulbs with (probably unintentional) decorative effect in the recess. There was seemingly much spring-cleaning to be done. They conducted their noisy love affairs chiefly underground. And again they were alone and uninterrupted.

Cool dry winds in March did not deter the small spring migrants. Black redstarts frequented the island all the

77

month. A male wheatear arrived on the 10th, a chiff-chaff on the 22nd, and the first ring-ousel on the 26th. Each was soon followed by others. The resident black-bird came to the peak of the house and woke us with song. He sang for nearly an hour each morning. Primroses and lesser celandines struggled into flower against the cool winds, and in the last days of March the delicate white petals of the scurvy-grass opened.

On the last night but one in March, for the sake of im-proving the ground for my sheep, I set fire to a meadow which had become overgrown with old, half-dead heather. I waited until I heard the first shearwaters before I struck a match. A fresh southerly wind encouraged the first flames, which soon spread. In a few minutes half an acre was burning, and a wide radius was filled with dancing red and yellow light. The smoke rolled away to leeward, low over the land.

The first shearwaters came flying into the light from the leeward side, the north coast of the island, head to wind, at 8 p.m. Soon there were hundreds. They looked beautiful by the warm light as they advanced slowly at various heights, some ten and some one hundred feet from the ground. They were leaning with fluttering wings, almost hovering, upon the strong wind. It was our first view of shearwaters flying freely at night.

They seemed fascinated by the flames, and again and again would poise over them, wings a-tremble like those of the hovering kestrel, and then retreat in this fixed head-to-wind position—the strength of the wind allowed this, and gave the impression that they were travelling, so to speak, in reverse gear. Others came forward more rapidly, gliding and flying at speed close to the fire; at times they seemed almost to touch the flames before suddenly shoot-ing upwards vertically and violently, until their white breasts vanished against the clouds. Probably some did this because, not apprehending the danger, they had sailed near enough to be singed.

The strong wind made the shearwaters seem more than usually alert. Thus, when they landed, they ran about quite actively, in contrast with their somewhat sluggish movements on calm nights. Their wings, held high over their heads and quivering in this position, helped them forward over the rough ground; and they climbed over the old stone hedge-walls with ease. They also made short runs upright on their toes, as they had done in my house, always resting full length on the breast afterwards. No doubt the fire had disturbed those nesting in that area, causing them to alight far from their holes; it was these we were able to watch performing so nimbly in the open. In the shadows beyond the fire other shearwaters were in and about their burrows more normally.

Although it had been a beautiful sight, I never started a heather fire on the island again at night, except in winter. I realized my mistake when on the morning after this fire I found some crows and gulls disputing over the burnt carcasses of two shearwaters.

The wheatears had built a nest in the garden wall and the storm-petrels had returned to the island at the end of April before Ada laid her egg in nest A in this second spring. I disturbed the shearwaters very little, contenting myself with a glance now and then, when, coming home from a hard day with the lobster pots, I was not too tired to climb the knoll and lift the sod.

This was physically a hard year for us on the island. A daughter had been born to us, and my wife was busy with her, in addition to the cares of the house. I had the garden, the fishing, and the sheep to attend to. So in the long summer days when I was lifting the pots here and there in the red bays and havens of the island, hoping for the miraculous haul of lobsters which the fishermen dream of, Hoofti II was born and grew up for the most part unwatched. I saw more of his parents, when, as the sun fell below the western sea, I returned to harbour from the fishing; at that hour the adult shearwaters would be gliding in to their assembly ground northwards of Skok-holm Head.

Hoofti II was well feathered in August when I placed a ring on his leg. His parents deserted him and in due course he slipped away to sea without further note or help from us.

*   *   *   *   *

In 1931 Adam and Ada returned to Burrow A for the third year in succession—in my knowledge of their exis-tence. Adam's ring was hanging half-open, and it was just luck, I thought, that it had survived the winter storms to this day of spring. Ada's ring was very worn, too, and the figures only just legible. Both rings were as thin as paper. We gave them new rings; Adam became RS 2256 and Ada RS 2246.

Of the other members of the village on the knoll only Caroline and one other 1929-ringed shearwater—the inter-loper AE 689 previously mentioned as frequenting nest B— were recovered this year. I changed their rings.

We were also disappointed not to recover Hoofti or Toofti or any other of the young birds ringed in the knoll in 1929 and 1930. I began to consider that it was likely that young birds did not return to land in their first year, and perhaps by the second year the rings would have dropped off, as had those of the adults after two seasons. We have seen that Adam was on the point of losing his after two years' wear; and Caroline actually dropped her ring outside her burrow in this spring. But of Caroline more in another chapter.

To return to Burrow A, to Adam and Ada and their bright new identification rings. At 10.40 p.m. on the 11th April 1931 I ran out of doors to investigate a scream-ing noise close to the front windows of the house. It was a calm, misty night. Dense fog banks had been rolling over the island all day. My torch illuminated a cone-shaped section of the moisture-laden air, the light falling on the grassy top of the garden wall—to discover a pair of shearwaters in the act of mating. The male appeared to be lying partly on top and partly on the right side of the female. He had a firm grip of the black feathers at the back of her head, and their tails were interlocked. Both were screaming excitedly, but the characteristic note seemed to have a special urgency fitting the occasion.

At first they ignored the light. When they separated a few seconds later I saw that they were both ringed. I picked them up and found that I had Adam and Ada in my hands.

The wall, of course, was only a few yards from the knoll burrows, yet it seemed strange that Adam and Ada should deliberately climb up there to celebrate this important annual ceremony. But at least it was an ideal, almost a romantic, site, high up and with plenty of manœuvring room, and free from possible interruption by rivals. Adam and Ada, I reflected, had always been rather exclusive in their domestic affairs.

This was my first view of mating shearwaters. Hitherto, if I had given the subject any thought at all, I had been inclined to suspect that this business took place out at sea, as it does in the case of the puffin. But here was proof otherwise, and the more I reflected the more it seemed likely that it was the desire to mate that helped to bring the shearwater back to the land in the spring. The shearwater does not sit about on the sea within sight, within stimulating sight, of its burrow, as does the puffin. The shearwater spends the day ranging up to hundreds of miles—as ringing later proved to us—from the land, and moreover it does not travel side by side closely with others of its kind (though areas of good fishing may attract a number together), but moves alone or widely separated from its companions. So that the chances of meeting its nest-mate at sea seem remote. No, I reflected, it must be the land, and especially the nest, which is the focal point, the well-remembered meeting and mating place.

Adam and Ada had somehow got up the wall, perhaps had alighted on it, in the blinding fog. They had done very well, I thought, to have got so near home at all. Some slight confusion of locality might under the circumstances be natural. Eyes alone could surely not have guided them home in the fog. There must be some other power. I determined to try to probe for the explanation, by experiment in the future.

Meanwhile here they were in my hands, and, having disturbed them, I must, in all fairness, see them safe home. To release them again on the wall might be fatal. Adam might, in his alarm, leap down into the darkness on one side of it and Ada the other, and so the loving pair would be separated at a critical hour.

I carried them back to their burrow and inserted them in its entrance. A moment later a muffled screaming told me they had resumed their intimacy, and I had been forgotten.

More than once in the succeeding years I found knoll shearwaters mating on the grassy crown of the garden wall. But more often mating took place in the nest itself; on these occasions it seemed to be a protracted affair—the lifted sod and the torch would reveal the noisy pair in the characteristic attitude. And once I found impatient lovers mating in the burrow before day had finished and the sun gone down.

It was nearly a month later that, on 4th May, Ada laid her egg. Adam took his turn as usual, brooding from the 6th to the 16th, over a long spell of light nights. I doubt if Ada visited him at night during this long spell; but if she did then I am sure she did not feed him, for he lost weight steadily. The change-over took place on the night of the 16th–17th. The period of moonlit and starlit nights continued. Ada, plump at first, remained on the nest for a week. She, too, lost weight. I was impressed by these long watches on the egg, and curious to know if Adam visited her at night, and if he did, whether he fed her.

Adam and Ada conducted some love affairs on the garden wall

*The foot of the shearwater spread over the egg, showing the
broad webbing below the sharp, keeled leg*

At 11 p.m. on the 19th I went out to the knoll colony. I remained watching there until dawn.

All that day there had been a heavy movement of migrating swallows, whitethroats, and spotted flycatchers. The swallows, with a single house-martin among them, had been flying north until well after sunset. They were late migrants, probably bound for the far north of Scotland and Norway, where they might have time only to rear one brood—our island ravens and blackbirds were already fledged. Each morning small migrants arrived on the island, rested for a while, and passed on. I hoped for a pleasant night listening for these migrants arriving or passing overhead.

The red light vanished from the west and a heavy dew covered the eiderdown in which I was wrapped. But it was still light, almost light enough to distinguish printed letters in my note-book, and much too light, I thought, for shearwaters. Storm-petrels flew over the garden wall. I could watch their bat-like forms plainly, as they darted over my head. Those on the wing were silent, but a low crooning came from the petrels lying in the crevices of the walls of the meadow—the number of these crooners contributed a regular anthem for the first three hours of the night, an everlasting purr like the song of the nightjar but lower in pitch.

The storm-petrels were my sole companions until at 1 a.m. a party of whimbrel flew over, making due north— their sweet tittering whistle receded in that direction. They went past close over my head, but I could not see them against the star-filled sky. Countrymen, hearing them thus on May nights of each year, have fancifully called them the Seven Whistlers.

The storm-petrels had vanished an hour later. At 2.30 a.m. a distant wheatear began singing. His notes suggested to me a crackling fire—perhaps because I had been thinking of one. The song leapt up and up like a growing flame, sharp and bright and jagged, only to die

G

down, to be still, and then to rise again. Other wheatears joined in, until flames seemed to be dancing all round the knoll. Then oyster-catchers and gulls were caught by the first pale colour lighting the north-east; their shrill yodelling began in earnest at 3 a.m. At 3.30 a.m. the skylark rose, drowning for me all other sounds with his rich loud song of morning. How heartening that outpouring was to me, stiff and cold and damp from my vigil! No other lark answered, for we have only one pair on the island. He was singing, I thought, for sheer happiness and not for other reason explained by the ornithologist in dull scientific jargon. Or did his sharp hearing catch the faint echo of the songs of rivals, of the other larks, away there three and four miles over the horizon, in mainland fields?

During the whole night not one shearwater had entered or left the village on the knoll. Nor did I hear a single shear-water call over the island. It was an important discovery. I was thus convinced that the adults do not feed each other at night, and that they are capable of sustained fasts while incubating the egg, during moonlit and starlit periods.

Adam returned and relieved Ada on the night of 24th May after Ada had spent a clear week incubating alone. Adam, it will be remembered, had spent ten days on the egg, apparently alone. Now, after a week's holiday at sea, he was a different bird, so solid to handle that I weighed him. He just turned the scale at 17 ounces—the heaviest record in my weighing data!

On 3rd June he was still on the egg, but had lost nearly two ounces in nine days of fasting. This was the final proof of the fasting of the shearwater. After all, it is not an unprecedented thing. We have already seen that the young bird does without food for ten or twelve days before flying to the sea. And it is said that the eider duck is never fed and never leaves the nest for the 28 days during which she incubates her eggs.

Though I handled them with loving care Adam and Ada became restless with my constant prying into their affairs.

I therefore avoided opening the burrow as much as possible. Instead I used match-sticks to keep account of the birds' movements. Two match-sticks placed upright in the entrance to the burrow sufficed. If a visit or an exchange had been made, these match-sticks were, of course, knocked down. And often I had to open the nest in order to retrieve these match-sticks—the adults had carried them in to add to the nest lining.

I took good care to glance at the egg towards the 50th day. I was rather surprised to find it pipped on the 49th day. However the chick had not hatched next day, it had merely enlarged the fracture with the little yellow hatching-tooth on the point of the upper mandible. On 24th June the chick was out of the egg, very fresh and damp, after 51 days of incubation.

Adam and Ada in turn brooded the chick for seven days. They then, as before, deserted it by day. They returned only on dark nights to feed the chick. I was soon to find that on moonlit nights the chick was not fed at all. Thus on thirteen nights during August up to the 26th of that month the chick was not fed. On the night of 26th August I found Adam alone with the chick. It was the 63rd day and it was the last feed. On the night of the 27th the chick, rather surprisingly, came to the mouth of the burrow, thus varying the procedure of other nestlings which we had had under observation. It did not fly, however, for ten more days. It was completely feathered, with no down showing, and had lost weight, by 5th September. It had disappeared next morning. Incubation period, 51 days; fledging, 74 days; total, 125 days.

* * * * *

In the following year, 1932, the first few shearwaters appeared on 6th February. I began to inquire into the affairs of the knoll colony during March. First Adam and then Ada was at home in the burrow. They were together on 21st March.

The knoll colony was rather congested this year. There were many fresh arrivals and these more than replaced those ringed birds which we posted as missing. New burrows were dug by the immigrants, and five out of the six original burrows were transformed by sectioning and altered almost out of recognition. At least eight eggs were laid in the nine nests which the colony now possessed, but not all these hatched.

Yet Adam and Ada preserved their independence and their home—with a little assistance from me. I frustrated the work of a neighbouring pair by filling with stones a shaft they were nightly driving towards the recess in which Ada had laid her egg. And so while some of the other pairs had indifferent luck with their eggs, Adam and Ada incubated in peace. They were now in their fourth breeding year and were my most valuable pair. I made every effort to see that they reared their chick, Hoofti IV, safely. And in this we were helped by the situation of the burrow. It had always been in rather a safe position against a rock on the western edge of the knoll, out of the hurly-burly of the centre.

To repeat the story of the incubation and rearing would only be wearisome. I found Hoofti IV the image of his predecessors. He received the like treatment. He was duly deserted by Adam and Ada. I ringed him and put him in the sea myself.

I hasten over this calm year, and come to 1933 and its mishaps and tragedies.

In 1933 shearwaters appeared like magic. Like the quails that covered the land they came at night to the knoll. I ringed more than forty in the little village there. Some of them were only passengers in the night, moving on because the congested village could not contain them. But others stayed and quarrelled and fought for homes. Eventually, instead of the normal six, I had twelve nests marked with lettered pegs and observation sods, and occupied by at least fifteen pairs or thirty birds.

Conditions in this year were, I thought, much as they are every year in the honeycomb near the lighthouse. That is, birds digging everywhere, one hole leading to another, and a perfect maze confronting and confusing the observer. But the birds, too, seemed thoroughly upset. As there were not enough holes to go round—fifteen pairs into twelve nests—four hens were compelled to share two nests, two in each. But they could by no means agree to incubate peaceably together—they quarrelled at night; and by day only one hen remained on the nest. Now a shear-water, with only one brood spot, can only incubate one egg at a time. The result was that the two eggs in one nest were each only half-incubated as the days passed. Nor could a hen distinguish her own egg. One of the eggs tended to be incubated more often than the other because it occupied the centre of the nest and was kept warm there, whereas the other egg, cold and dirty, tended to be pushed farther and farther away into the corners of the recess, or even some distance down the passage. Occasionally it would be retrieved at night by the incoming birds, and might then be shuffled about quite fortuitously during the domestic squabble until it had taken the place of the warm egg.

From the very beginning I had marked and dated every egg laid in the knoll village, with indelible pencil.

The eggs in these double nests never hatched. About half-way through the incubation period I removed one from each nest and placed it in a nest from which the egg had been lost or in which the hen had not laid at all. I hoped thus to save the lives within the shells. But by then the four eggs had received such a series of chillings that the embryos had perished.

In four out of the twelve burrows no eggs were laid at all, though birds—chiefly different individuals, some from other burrows—frequented the nests until July.

Ada herself did not return this year. I could not trace her among the forty odd birds registered in the village this year. She had probably died, had been killed at sea in winter, had suffered almost certainly that swift natural death which ends the lives of most oceanic birds. Poor Ada! We mourned her, but as her disappearance only gradually became a certainty, the blow was not a sudden one. But it was heavy enough.

Of course, there is a possibility that Ada had lost her ring in the winter, and that the unringed lady which Adam took up with in 1933 was really Ada. But I cannot easily think so. Adam's ring was still firm and legible this spring, and if this unringed female really was Ada her ring should have been on her leg and in a like state of preservation. Somehow, too, the new bird did not seem like Ada in the least. She was shyer than Ada had been, she was less tolerant of my intrusions, my handling, and my fond conversations. She was much wilder, and ran off down the burrow when Ada, in previous years, would have sat eyeing me with indifference.

Adam and his new consort spent the first three days of April in Burrow A. Excavations were going on nightly at a furious pace in the village. A shaft from outside was again struck towards Burrow A, while another shaft from inside the burrow was aimed, unconsciously no doubt, to meet it. I gave up trying to isolate the old burrows. After all, I thought, what business have I to interfere with village affairs? The shearwaters were on the knoll ages ago, and they will be there ages after I am gone, and for me to suppose that by supervising and manipulating their domestic architecture I can improve their condition materially is vain and ridiculous.

Rather absurd, too, was our decision to give Adam's second wife the name of Baby. Adam and his new wife removed presently from Burrow A to Burrow B. So his new wife, by this removal, became known as AB to us; and this deteriorated easily to Baby, especially as she was obviously a young and inexperienced housekeeper. I'm afraid we considered Baby a very poor fish compared with the late lamented Ada. For instance we were inclined—without adequate reason, for Adam may have decided on the removal himself—to blame Baby for allowing another pair (a strong young couple) to hustle them out of Burrow A. Adam and Baby fled to the enlarged and altered Burrow B. There, after some sharp exchanges with Caroline and her consort, who had begun the season by occupying this nest, Adam and Baby were able to settle down to the quiet days of incubation.

Baby laid her egg on 10th May. But she seemed restless and dissatisfied with her new life. On the second and fourth days the egg was deserted, and in the days of the succeeding month it was frequently left alone by day. I do not know whether this was because other shearwaters interfered with the burrow at night. It might have been that my almost daily peep made her so restless. She was certainly making a mess of things. Perhaps she was too young to take the responsibilities of parenthood seriously? At any rate she was only discovered incubating on three out of sixteen days on which I paid a visit to Burrow B. Adam did his full share, but no more, and on days when Baby should have been on the job but instead was gallivanting at sea, Adam left the egg cold. My imagination pictured Adam as an indignant and sorrowing husband.

The egg, of course, did not hatch.

In July Adam and Baby went away to sea altogether. I flung the cracked and stinking egg to the winds.

* * * * *

Adam was old now. I felt this especially when he returned in 1934. He was the first bird on my books, and, apart from Caroline, was the sole survivor of 1929. It seemed to me likely, in the light of gathering evidence, that a shearwater does not breed until at least two years of age. Baby might have been one or two years old in 1933—we have seen that she was not enthusiastic in her (probably) first breeding year. Let us, at any rate, suppose that a shearwater is two years old before breeding begins. Adam, on this reckoning therefore, was seven years old in 1934. But he was a vigorous and successful breeder in a well-established burrow in 1929, so it might well be that in 1934 he was actually ten, fifteen, or twenty years old. He was perhaps attaining a ripe old age for a shearwater. The webs of his feet were split and ragged, he had lost two claws from his left foot, and the toes of his right foot had been nipped right off for about half an inch—a clean bite as if a fish had snapped off these extremities. The single claw on the left foot was worn and short. Adam was no longer young.

Adam returned to Burrow B rather late in 1934. During a SSE. gale on 14th April I found him there in company with Caroline. It was not the first time that he had met this lady of his own age, this neighbour; but these occasions of past years had nevertheless been rare, and always, I had thought, accidental. They had by chance come together for the day in the same shelter, as had often happened with two otherwise unrelated birds. So I did not at once attach importance to the discovery of these old-timers sitting side by side in Burrow B. They would soon be separated and living with their young mates of last year.

But Caroline's mate of 1933 did not turn up, nor at first did Baby. Adam and Caroline settled down to long conversations in the nest. Over the period of the April new moon they were there each night, busy lining the nest with the bulbs and the pale-green underground swords of the bluebell, with grass, and with odds and ends. They were busy and talkative. You could imagine them talking of old times as you listened to their cackling under the sod. And it looked as if they were going to make a do of it, as the saying is. The freshness of early love might not be theirs, or so I fancied. They were an old, a life-toughened pair, but with the spring even an old stager's thoughts may turn to . . .

Adam mated with Caroline. I caught them in the act when I opened the nest one night late in April.

They were a tame, a delightful pair. I was very happy that they had made it up for a partnership. Long may they live together, I prayed. But this prayer, as we shall see, was vain.

Caroline's claws were still fairly long and sharp, and her webs unscathed, so I judged her to be younger than Adam. She would, I hoped, keep the home tidy and decent for the ageing Adam in the years to come. (These pretty little thoughts came to me from time to time, and, although I knew that I was being entirely unscientific and sentimental, they relieved some of the tedium of watching year by year.) Caroline made a good start that summer by laying a large white egg on 1st May. I judged and hoped that she could go on laying for years yet.

This judgment and hope were justified. Caroline lived many more years. For that matter she may still be alive.

April 1934 had been a disappointing month, full of cold winds—a backward time. 1st May broke warm and calm. I spent part of that May day lying full length in Mad Bay watching the young ravens at their nest in a long crack in the red cliff. The sea moved with a quiet chuckle in and out of the rocks far below. A pair of razor-bills had come in at the lower end of the raven crack, on the ground floor, so to speak; and they were displaying with pretty wing and head movements, their yellow mouths partly opened.

Towards sunset I returned across the island, looking in at the village on the knoll on the way to the back door of my house.

Each year I had had to do a certain amount of reconstruction among the nests. I generally did this spring-cleaning in February, before the majority of the shearwaters had returned. I had to cut new observation sods to replace the old, which were worn with use and perhaps fallen in with sheep-treading or heavy rains and winter gales. The observation sod had in fact become a problem. Being lifted so frequently, it got damaged, gradually disintegrating day after day. Pieces would fall off from both the sod and the sides of the hole it fitted into. At last I had to devise an improved housing scheme for the village. I used a bottomless box to take the place of the natural recess. I bedded the box deep in upside down, so that the passage was opposite a hole cut in the side of the box. Another hole in the top (really the bottom) of the box was for inspection, and this I covered first with a slate and over the slate a thick sod. I attached a chain to the slate, passing it through the sod, so that I had a convenient handle for lifting the two as one piece, as one inspection cover to the nest. The box was thus hidden from view underground, and the slate prevented any part of the sod dropping into the nest.

This was much better, although some energetic birds dug through the floor at times, or sent a shaft to one side of the box. In later seasons I countered much of this side-tracking work by lining the tunnels with wooden walls and ceilings, and to these the shearwaters raised no serious objection. After all, if they could nest in the earthenware drain-pipes on the island, as well as in crevices in the solid rock, they would not reject my home-made, wooden-walled, earth-floored passages and homes. They did not.

In 1934 I had repaired the principal burrows in the knoll village; and now on 1st May here was Caroline sitting on her new-laid egg in Burrow B. I lifted her from her bulb-lined nest, noted her ring number, caressed her, and replaced her. I marked her egg, and closed the nest.

Caroline's story is only half told. It is long, and I must leave it to another chapter. Let us here take leave of that good old fighter Adam. He and Caroline spent an ideal summer sharing the work of incubation equally. They brought up Hoofti V splendidly—to the usual point of desertion. I ringed Hoofti V and he went to the sea a week or so after Adam and Caroline had vanished.

Of the three, Adam and Hoofti V had vanished for ever.

*   *   *   *   *

There are two postscripts, the first concerning that little minx Baby.

Surprisingly Baby put in an appearance in 1934 after all. By previously established shearwater law Adam, having in Baby a living wife, should not have taken Caroline to wed, and so committed bigamy. There was no precedent in my careful register of the knoll marriages. No; only if one party died or disappeared from the village might the other take a new mate.

However, there appeared to be extenuating circumstances.

I do not know what Baby was about in that year. She appeared once only, and very late; to be exact, on 15th May, in Burrow A, a fortnight after Caroline had laid her egg in Burrow B. Baby might have appeared earlier in the village, for of course I did not knock at all the doors each day or night; but I did not see her before or after 15th May. On that day she was in Burrow A with a new, an unringed bird, a gentleman with whom she subsequently mated in 1935. Where this pair eloped to—if they did elope—during 1934 is unknown to me; they vanished completely until 1935, when they returned and successfully reared a young one. In 1936—and since we have gone so far we may as well complete the card-indexed story of this pair—Baby's mate of 1935 had vanished; he had either removed out of the colony or had lost his life at sea. I never saw him again. Baby took a fresh husband (the third) in 1936.

In July of that year I had occasion to collect some shearwaters for a homing test. I put Baby in the crate which was going on the ship for Africa. But she was never released. She ended her unsatisfactory career by suddenly dying in the tropic of Cancer.

* * * * *

The second postscript concerns Hoofti V. When he was just over a fortnight old he was exhibited to the members of the Eighth International Ornithological Congress, which visited the island on 8th July 1934. He was a little ball of slate-grey down then, and his dull eye probably took in little of the stares of the peoples of so many nations who marched past along the edge of the temporarily railed-off knoll colony.

'A strange little bird.' 'A dear little thing.' These were the smiling greetings he got—in Dutch, French, Italian, German, Spanish, Norwegian, Bulgarian, Hungarian, Latvian, English of many overseas kinds, and so many other languages. There were nearly two hundred people to look at the ball in my hand. And I thought that if Hoofti V could have seen with my eye he would have said inwardly, as I did: 'A strange crowd; but look, how wonderfully happy they are to see Hoofti V on this lovely day; why, a mere bird can smash all petty nationalism; all the world has become one man to pay homage to a fragile morsel of life, a nestling bird!'

Then came a command performance. Ex-king Ferdinand of Bulgaria was sitting in a camp chair in a truly regal position on the knoll, under our flagstaff, which we had decorated like a maypole with the flags of all nations. Ferdinand had suppressed the fierce daggers of his gout, and, with the help of his attendants and his charming niece the Princess Victoria of Leiningen, had fought his way foot by foot to the crown of the knoll. There, while the other members of the congress roamed the island for an hour looking at the other sea-birds, he could sit resting in the cool north wind, and watch the gulls, the oyster-catchers, the puffins, and the flowers at all points of the compass about him. But walk a step farther this aged ornithologist dared not. I was asked to bring Hoofti V to his hand.

'*Puffinus anglorum!* The young bird of *Puffinus anglorum*! Wonderful, wonderful! Yes, it is beautiful!'

The long fingers of this German prince, this ex-king of the Bulgars, those fingers that had signed treaties and letters of state and other scraps of paper, stroked the fine down of the child of Adam and Caroline admiringly, even —I feared—covetously.

The princess could not at first let Hoofti return to his burrow. 'No, no; he is not a bird! He is something else; a what do you call him? A goblin, yes? And the mother, she is not here? You say she is on the sea all day, and it is not cold for him without her? In that dark damp place in the earth?'

Hoofti V was returned to his nest at last and the sod closed over Burrow B. For a while the princess, who was interested in botany, collected the dwarf flowers about the knoll; centaury, pimpernel, speedwell, rock-spurrey, sheep's sorrel, and wood-sage. An hour later the congress returned in small boats to the destroyers lying at anchor in the bight of South Haven, between Wreck Cove and the Devil's Teeth. The angry gulls settled down in peace on the plateau once more, and Hoofti V resumed his long siesta.

CHAPTER IX

CAROLINE

IT is Caroline's turn, for that band of shearwaters ringed in the village on the knoll in the first year of this study (1929), she alone has survived to the day of my writing this.

I have described, in Chapter VII, how Carol and Caroline reared a young bird in nest C in 1929. I have not described how they fared in 1930 and afterwards. In 1930, that year when we islanders were so busy, Caroline was at home in Burrow C with a new bird, on 26th March. But on the 29th and 30th she was with her true mate Carol. The observation sod was trodden in by sheep next day, and though I patched it up it continually fell in. I blame myself now for not cutting a new sod at once, to fit over the recess, but at the time I had so many other things to do that I kept putting off this simple little task. The result was that part of the passage of Burrow C got trodden down too. Carol and Caroline frequented the nest in spite of this; but the broken sod and the spoilt passage admitted light to the recess. If ever an egg was laid—as I believe it must have been—it was soon lost. The shearwaters were not happy brooding if light came directly into the recess. It is most likely that the egg was stolen when the sod collapsed soon after the egg was laid. Crows flying overhead would instantly swoop down on such a tit-bit.

Burrow C in fact was a failure in 1930.

In 1931, even before I had begun to inquire into village affairs and assist in the spring cleaning, the inhabitants had abandoned the ruin of Burrow C, and were starting a new shaft in the direction of Burrow F, using, however, the same entrance, which had preserved its original shape. On the afternoon of 5th May I sank a new observation shaft over the new recess, to find the burrow completed and the nest lined; but there were no birds present.

That same night I paid calls in the village. I picked up Caroline's ring in the mouth of the burrow, this Burrow C. Inside were two unringed birds.

Now that dropped ring had not been there in the day. Obviously it had just been dropped by one of the birds now in the recess. Probably, hanging loose on the leg, it had been knocked off as Caroline shuffled into the burrow. It was Caroline's ring all right—AE 688—just legible but worn as thin as brown paper. As mentioned earlier, we had not at first realized how swiftly the rings wore out. This ring had had two years' wear and was finished; it should have been changed after one year's use.

But one of the pair in the burrow was almost certainly Caroline. The other was very much less certainly Carol. Since male and female shearwater are so alike externally, the only way to discover Caroline was to ring both and find out later, by some clue to sex, which was female of the pair. I gave both new rings: RS 2247 and RS 2251.

On 14th May RS 2247 was sitting on a spotlessly white new-laid egg. I was delighted to welcome her as the nearly-but-not-quite-lost Caroline. She sat for two days. Then RS 2251 took over for seven days.

I could now never be sure that RS 2251 was the original Carol, though I hoped and half-believed he was from his behaviour. He was tame and well-behaved, as good a mate as the original Carol, and just as uxorious. However, scientifically, he was 'not proven.' So I had to give him the title of ? Carol.

There was one 'at home' during incubation when ? Carol sat out the day with Caroline. They shared the brooding in the usual long irregular spells, according to the state of the moon. The chick was safely hatched in 52 days.

This nestling narrowly escaped drowning, a curious death for a shearwater. September 1931 opened cold and wet.

A cloud-burst flooded the low-lying homes of the knoll, including Burrow C. The rising water drove Caroline's chick out of the burrow only three days after desertion. On this day, his 63rd, we found him (we had ringed him nine days before) sitting in front of our kitchen window. His long down was mucky with wet earth accumulated in his scramble to the surface, to air. The appeal in that forlorn little figure, trying to hide from the steaming sunlight, was answered. We put him in the sea, a little prematurely perhaps, but he paddled and dived and swam away under water with the skill of a mature fledgeling.

*　　　*　　　*　　　*　　　*

? Carol and Caroline again won a home in nest C in 1932. They started lining the nest in March, after constant bickerings and interruptions from some of the many strangers which settled in (or called in passing through) the village that year. They reared their third chick with difficulty, for, owing to the hazards of being lost once or twice down the gangway during excavations, the egg hatched very late, after an unnaturally long incubation period of 56 days, and the chick was at first very weak. It could scarcely lift its head from the ground, on which it rested the point of its bill continually, as does the feeble new-born storm-petrel.

? Carol and Caroline nursed it well, however, and when I last saw it in September 1932 it was well grown and almost free from down.

*　　　*　　　*　　　*　　　*

The years were gliding by. On 1st April 1933 I recovered ? Carol and Caroline sitting together in nest B. But they returned later to their old home in Burrow C.

This was the year of fifteen pairs in twelve nests. ? Carol and Caroline were again having a struggle to maintain their dignity as old-established villagers. The burrowing and enlarging that went on must have caused them annoyance and great inconvenience, though they too took a share in the digging—at times I found their bills coated with earth when I recovered them at night. But they stuck doggedly to their Burrow C, and there Caroline laid her egg on 13th May. On the 16th a shaft driven from the recess of Burrow E penetrated the recess of Burrow C where Caroline was incubating—as it happened on that day in company with ? Carol.

Nest C became one with nest E, became an affair of one recess and two entrances, to be used by more than the former tenants of C and E.

On 22nd May ? Carol and Caroline and their egg had vanished completely. I could not find the egg even by groping far down the passages. Instead, a female, which I had ringed on a fresh egg in nest H, was in the recess, alone. After that ? Carol and Caroline only returned at night occasionally. You might fancy that they were unhappy over the cruel interruption and loss—from their behaviour. They wandered at night in and out of the homes of the other villagers. For instance, on 28th May ? Carol crouched by himself in his shattered home, the burrow we now called CE, while Caroline was satisfying her maternal hunger *by incubating an egg in nest G.*

Good old Caroline!

But she was not allowed to indulge in this pleasure for long. She had only been able to keep this egg warm for one day, either because the lawful owners had temporarily neglected it or because she had bullied one or both of them off it. The truth of this will hardly be known. Next day Caroline had vanished, and a legitimate parent was in possession, and remained in possession. This egg in nest G hatched off, and the chick was one of few successfully reared in the village that year.

On 16th June ? Carol and Caroline were at home together. They seemed suddenly to have resumed their love-making. They were billing and cooing in the old nest. But from previous experience I had no expectation of a second egg.

H

Imagine, then, my surprise on finding the pair together again on 20th June, and Caroline sitting hard on an egg!

It turned out to be a stale egg, however. It was dirty, thickly coated with earth. I scraped it clean—to discover on it the legend 'RS 2298, 13th May.' This represented the number of the new ring which had been given to Caroline, and the date on which the egg had been laid. So it was Caroline's egg. Somehow it had been buried where I had not been able to locate it. It had been retrieved just as mysteriously.

It was a short-lived effort. Caroline incubated the egg for three days. On the fourth day she and the egg had again vanished. It was now past midsummer by two days.

? Carol and Caroline went away to sea, and, having nothing better to do, they probably started their annual moult early.

? Carol never returned.

In the spring of 1934 Caroline and Adam joined together in matrimony. Their short but successful partnership of one season has already been described in the preceding chapter.

*   *   *   *   *

Carol, ? Carol, and Adam had vanished. In 1935 Caroline chose for a mate Carol II, a new bird who, like Adam, was to last for one season only.

Carol II and Caroline did not seem to hit it off at all well. Caroline's egg never hatched. Again there was burrowing which disturbed nest CE. It lost all semblance of its original state as nest C. The egg was lost and retrieved and lost again, as it had been in 1933. Carol II was a shy bird, he was probably not two and certainly not three years old (he had a new look, with clean sharp-clawed legs), in his first breeding season, and if so this might have contributed to the disaster.

In 1936 he returned to the knoll, but not once did I find him with Caroline. Carol II took up, instead, with a new lady elsewhere in the village, and to her he has ever since

been faithfully, if bigamously, attached. Caroline was, in
fact, having bad luck with her husbands. The desertion
of or by Carol II was a new thing in her career; hitherto
she had chosen husbands from bachelors or widowers in
the village, and had remained faithful to them as long as
they lived. Now, while remaining faithful to her ancient
marriage-bed, the altered nest C, she took in 1936 a new
mate, an unringed bird and presumably therefore a
youngster without experience. With him, whom we
must call Carol III, she successfully reared a chick in
1936 and 1937.

Carol III failed to turn up in 1938. Caroline then took
her sixth male to wed, Carol IV, a gentleman who had put
in a preliminary appearance in 1937, when I had found
him, a stranger, and ringed him on 10th July. We may
guess from this midsummer appearance that he had then
been sexually immature; he was exploring the ground
for another season. And his preliminary canter for the
marriage stakes was successful. Carol IV mated with
Caroline in 1938 and reared a lusty chick in nest CE.

*   *   *   *   *

In 1939 Caroline and Carol IV were together again.
Caroline was now at least eleven, and probably twelve,
years old, possibly much older. On 10th April she was
in the nest with RS 2305, a 1933-ringed bird. This however was only a characteristic village visit, a day for gossip
with a neighbour (you might fancy) before settling down
for the season.

On 7th May 1939 I saw Caroline for the last time. She
was then in her ancient nest in the Burrow CE, and with
Carol IV. I have not met her since. I hope my fear that
she has died of an accident at sea is unfounded, but some
things point to this. Why else should Carol IV take up
with a new wife on 19th May, and in nest F? There were
eight nests in the village this year, and after the disappearance of Caroline nest CE was much frequented by other

pairs, but no egg was laid in it, and it eventually fell in altogether—it had become very dilapidated during the years.

Carol IV and his new wife, a young bird previously unrecorded on our books, did a curious thing in nest F. They seized the egg of a young female who had laid there on 24th May. Next day this egg was deserted and cold and had rolled out near the entrance. There it remained, cold, until the 29th, when Carol IV had retrieved it and was sitting on it. Next day AT 347, the owner of the egg, was incubating. On 2nd June the nest was empty and the egg cold. On 5th June Carol IV's new wife (312577) was in the nest, but the egg had again rolled down the passage. It was restored, and next day Carol IV was sitting beside it, not on it—the egg was cold. On the 7th Carol IV and his wife sat *beside* the egg—it was therefore still cold. Of course the egg never hatched, though after this the pair did keep it warm for a fortnight.

In June 1939 my wife and I went abroad in search of shearwaters, and observations at the knoll were made by a friend who took charge of the island in our absence. But night after night before we left I had searched the village for my beloved Caroline.

I could not believe that we should see her no more.

Caroline in her last year was vigorous and bright-eyed

Hurrying back into her hole again. Note the ring

CHAPTER X

AGE—AND OTHER PROBLEMS

WE have recited instances of the incubation and fledging period often enough to make further accounts tedious, more especially as the chain of essential events never varied. From the total of all the records it is possible to say that the incubation period averaged 51 days and that of fledging 72 days.

We have seen, too, how faithful, under difficult conditions at times, the adult is to its mate. As a rule as long as the pair lived through the winter and returned to the village in the spring the same male joined with the same female, even though at first for some days and nights one might be present in the village and the other absent. There is little doubt that the knoll and its special topographical features are well remembered by the shearwater homing to it for the first time each year. The swallow remembers the farm where it nested the previous year, and, as the swallow finds its old nest and mate at the rafters of the cart-shed, so the shearwater enters its old burrow on the knoll, there to hear and to find its old mate of last year.

But in the early spring days, in March and April, when the shearwaters are spring-cleaning their burrows, there is much apparently indiscriminate visiting going on. At first no one bird seems quite certain of its mate or its burrow. At least that is the superficial conclusion to be drawn from the appearance of one bird now in one burrow, now in another, now alone, now with its mate, but often spending a day, a day and a night, or even two days, with some other member of the colony. It is therefore remarkable that in all this hurly-burly, this kind of postman's knock, the old birds eventually set to their old partners and settle down to the essential tasks once more.   There should be, one feels, more mistakes, more strife, and especially more interchanging, accidental or deliberate, of partners — if it is true that the old burrow is the sole medium by which the marriage ties are faithfully renewed.

In fact I believe that the old home in the village, though important, is not the deciding factor.   We have seen that one pair may move from one burrow to another as the years pass—and I could give many instances of this—and also we have seen that the burrows change shape with the constant excavating, and some burrows cave in altogether. A burrow is therefore rather an unstable rendezvous.

It is more likely that voice is the principal factor by which individuals recognize each other.   Even my dull human ear can quite easily detect the variation in the screams of individuals.   Some shearwaters have very distinctive cries. Night after night we would hear and recognize one or two of these special performers as they flew past over the house-top, or bellowed from inside a burrow.   Adam had had a notable cry.   While the screams of other shearwaters were more subtly but certainly distinct.

The adult bird of any species recognizes the individual cries of its young.   Even more surely must it know the voice of its mate.

In the early part of the night as much and often more noise comes from the shearwaters underground than from those on the wing.   These birds in the breeding holes are announcing their presence and situation to the incoming birds.   One answers another excitedly.   The homing bird, having located approximately the region of the island where lie the burrows in which its mate is waiting, soon hears a familiar voice coming from underground, the voice of a mate which he has seldom seen (certainly not clearly in daylight as far as we know), and he answers this cry of a body to which he is drawn by the memory of pleasurable contacts, of past hours of courting and mating.   In the case of the untried breeder an instinctive hope probably takes the place of this pleasant recollection.

Seeing is not necessarily believing in the case of the shearwater on land. Hearing and feeling are more important in the blackness of the burrow. Hearing and feeling enable the shearwater to pair for life.

We can glance briefly at the exceptions that prove the rule of pairing for life. Two I have already quoted: the instance of the somewhat flighty young lady, Baby, who, mating with Adam in 1933, failed to rear a chick then, and who, in 1934, associated with a stranger while Adam took Caroline to wife for the first and last time; and the case of Carol II and Caroline who, after an unsuccessful year in 1935, parted, and in 1936 mated with new partners.

I can add that as the seasons rolled on other instances of infidelity occurred in the knoll village. As a typical instance, after two years of faithful collaboration one pair dissolved partnership, the female taking up with a new male to which she remained faithful for four years until she vanished after 1936; while the male did exactly the same thing, that is, took up with a new female and lived with her for four seasons until he failed to return in 1937. This was a rare case from among my most valuable birds; but there were a few other instances among less important, more fugitive members of the village. Perhaps the most common case was that of a new pair one year mating with fresh immigrants in the next season. Nevertheless these irregularities were very much in the minority among the one hundred odd matings which were celebrated in the knoll community in twelve years.

*   *   *   *   *

How long is the life of the Manx shearwater?

Caroline had bred for eleven seasons before she vanished from the village. She was therefore, when seen for the last time in May 1939, at least twelve years old, probably thirteen, and possibly older still.

At the time of writing, spring 1940, there are nine pairs of shearwaters in the eight eligible nests on the knoll. The oldest bird now is RS 2262, which has bred for ten seasons (including 1940). The ages (in breeding seasons) of the remaining seventeen birds are as follows: three have bred eight times, one seven, five five times, four four times, one three times, and three twice. No account is taken of one or two young birds which have failed to secure partners and have only appeared spasmodically in the village in various years.

The average of these shearwaters surviving in the village is therefore 91 divided by 18=five summers.

This is higher than the average life of shearwaters which have appeared as newcomers, bred so many summers in the village, and then vanished. I have complete longevity records of exactly twenty birds which have dwelt thus in the village. The sum of their summers is 77, and the average is therefore 3·85 summers. Again no account is taken of spasmodic visitors which failed to breed in these completed years.

Seven birds which were in the village when I began this study (that is to say, Ada and Adam, Bill and Bess, Carol and Caroline, and the intruder AE 689) spent between them a total of 30 summers there. The average of these incomplete ages is therefore 4·3 summers. This figure, higher than the average of the twenty complete lives, is influenced by Caroline's eleven summers.

Taking the three figures, we find that the average of all the shearwaters which have bred and/or are still breeding in the knoll is 4·4 summers. Allowing that the shearwater is at least one, and often two, years old when it first arrives in breeding condition—and I shall later give what evidence I possess about this—we can say that the minimum average life of the Manx shearwater is six years.

There is no evidence to suggest that the world population of the Manx shearwater is increasing or decreasing. As far as we know it is stationary. Therefore it is only necessary for the maintenance of the species that each adult should produce to breeding age one of its kind once only in its lifetime of six years. That is, in the 4·4 breeding seasons, only one young bird has to be reared to maturity, or roughly one youngster in four seasons. But it takes two birds to make a breeding pair. Each pair of shearwaters must therefore rear two young birds in four seasons; that is, each colony must rear fifty per cent of chicks from all eggs laid. And in practice I found that about fifty per cent of the eggs hatched in the knoll colony each year. But the ratio of matured chicks to breeding pairs in the knoll was, I feel sure, somewhat affected by the constant interference caused by my observation at the nests. In some years when I interfered little, more chicks got off; in other seasons when I was constantly on the probe, fewer chicks were reared. It will be safe to allow another ten per cent for interference, and to say that about sixty per cent of the eggs laid by the Manx shearwater normally result in matured chicks. And this ten per cent is only the smallest margin which we require for the casualties which are known to occur between desertion stage and first breeding season.

The margin is in fact so slender that we can say without hesitation that the average life of the Manx shearwater is *at least* six years. Seven years will give the bird a better margin, a longer time in which to rear its replacement, but we shall stick to this minimum average of six years which we have worked out from the data furnished by the villagers of the knoll. And we can add that individual shearwaters may reach twice that age, as did Caroline, and as may the eleven-year-old RS 2262.

Information as to length of life in wild birds is very scarce. In captivity birds sometimes reach remarkable ages, though the majority may die early; but we are only concerned here with the life of the wild bird. Without ringing it is impossible to obtain longevity records, and without an unbroken series of observations over many years, such as we have carried out in the knoll village, it is impossible to obtain figures for the average life of the wild bird. I know of no other similar data on sea-birds with which the ages of my shearwaters can be compared. Mrs Nice has studied the American song-sparrow and found that its average expectation of life is probably less than two and a half years. And in general it is considered that small passerine birds live very short lives.

There is, however, a widespread belief that the sea-bird lives a long time. A herring-gull in captivity has lived fifty years, and an eagle-owl seventy-four years. In 1888 Maynard dissected a gannet and decided that it had lived at least 140 years, a figure he arrived at simply by counting the ruptured follicles or egg-receptacles in the bird's ovaries. As the gannet takes four or five years to reach breeding condition and is obviously a long-lived bird, it was, at the time, thought that Maynard might be right. However, it is now known that every empty follicle in the ovary does not represent an egg laid; on the contrary, many ova, after going through an early stage of ripening, fail to mature further, but are resorbed, with their investing receptacles, and become mere pieces of connective tissue. So, while it is possible to count these pieces of tissue, these resorbed follicles, both the unmatured and the ovulated kinds together, it is not admissible to suppose that the result represents the total number of eggs laid by the bird. The number of these resorbed follicles can only be a rough guide to the bird's age.

Wynne Edwards,[1] examining the ovaries of fulmar petrels taken in northern Labrador on 26th July, has recently drawn some interesting conclusions as to the age and breeding of the tube-nosed birds, to which our shearwater belongs. He considers that all these birds taken at that place on that day were non-breeding birds, and he concludes from this and from other evidence that about twenty

[1] *Proceedings of the Zoological Society*, London, series A, vol. 109, parts 2 and 3, 1939, pp. 127–32.

per cent of the fulmar petrel population remains at large in the North Atlantic during the breeding season.   He considers it may be proved that most of the tube-nosed birds do not breed regularly each year, but only intermittently, and, in the case of the fulmar, probably on an average once in three years.   These observations he hinges partly on his discovery that the length of the middle claw of a fulmar's foot bears a relation (as he says) to the age of the bird. Very reasonably he presumes that the claws cannot be worn down at sea; they can only be worn down when the bird comes to land to breed, when its claws make contact with the rocky cliff on which the fulmar nests.   And for confirmation he has found that the ovaries of those birds with the shortest claws contain the greatest number of resorbed follicles, i.e. the greatest number of both ovulated and unmatured receptacles.

I quote Wynne Edwards's table for the four 'non-breeding' female fulmars which he examined:

Specimen	Middle Claws	Resorbed Follicles	
1	15·8 mm.	about	29
2	15·6 ,,	,,	28
3	13·0 ,,	,,	50
4	10·6 ,,	,,	101

Although, as remarked before, it is not known how many of the resorbed follicles represent eggs actually laid, Wynne Edwards suggests that (on the basis that the fulmar breeds only every third year) specimen 4 was approaching 100 years of age.   Now a fulmar does not, as far as we know, breed in its first few years.   Say, then, that it is four years old when it lays its first egg.   In one hundred years, laying every third year, it will have laid 32 eggs. Thus we can try to arrive at the relation of eggs laid to resorbed follicles, and to length of claw.

There are weaknesses in this method of calculation. Some fulmars, like some shearwaters, nest in bare rocky situations where their claws must suffer far more wear than those of fulmars and shearwaters which lay their egg on soft turf and earth. Watching nesting fulmars at Lambay Island, I noted that almost all of them were breeding on ledges covered with long soft grass which would have no effect on their claws; while on the mainland of Pembrokeshire fulmars are to be seen breeding on the hardest basaltic cliff. So it is with shearwaters: most of the knoll villagers have homes in soft peaty ground, but beyond the knoll many holes in the bare rock are occupied by shearwaters. Again, while looking at fulmars in Iceland, I was surprised to find many adults were incubating two eggs. I do not know if these eggs were the produce of two hens, but in each instance I found only one bird incubating. If some birds can lay two eggs this will upset Wynne Edwards's calculation, though it is true that, as far as I know, only a small minority of fulmars lay (or incubate) two eggs.

Nevertheless the possibility of telling a bird's age by claw measurements struck me as important, and I immediately went to the knoll to measure the middle claws of the shearwaters incubating there. I found that there was little difference in length between the right and the left middle claws on any one bird. I give the measurements therefore of the middle claw on the right foot of each bird, together with the bird's age (taken from the ringing books, and with one year added to cover the adolescent period).

Ring number	Age	Middle claw	Year first bred
RS 2262	10 years	5·5 mm.	1931
RS 2305	8 ,,	8·5 ,,	1933
RS 2313	8 ,,	8·0 ,,	1933
RS 2317	8 ,,	9·0 ,,	1933
RV 7482	7 ,,	8·5 ,,	1934
RW 7491	5 ,,	9·0 ,,	1936
300342	4 ,,	8·0 ,,	1937
300240	4 ,,	7·5 ,,	1937
EXP 103	4 ,,	8·5 ,,	1937
307933	3 ,,	8·0 ,,	1938
AT 347	2 ,,	9·0 ,,	1939

It is curious that both RS 2262 and AT 347, the oldest and youngest on this list, had the left foot bitten off half-way over the webs, so that there were no claws left on that foot. While RS 2262 also had both outside toes nipped off the right foot, leaving a single small middle claw available for measurement. Had this loss of five out of six claws affected the length of the last claw? Had the bird been forced to work this claw excessively, and so reduced it to 5·5 mm.? The nine other measurements show no gradation with age. Claw-length in the Manx shearwater seems to give no reliable indication as to age.

* * * * *

We now come to the question of intermittent breeding. Among the largest Tubinares, the albatrosses, intermittent breeding is known to be a normal fixed habit. The largest of all, the wandering albatross, *Diomedea exulans*, cannot breed more than once in two years because after the young hatch in the late summer they remain at the nest a whole year, being fed at intervals summer and winter by their parents, who are consequently occupied in domestic cares for something like eighteen months at a stretch. Thus in a colony of these albatrosses it is usual to find, during the cool Antarctic summer, pairs with their single egg, and other pairs with well grown young. Here is the romance of ornithology—we wonder at the stoicism of the young albatross in facing the vile Antarctic winter with its blizzards and low temperatures; its parents do no more than feed it occasionally and it remains alone and unbrooded in the nest once it has grown its feathers.

The lives of the tube-nosed birds are astonishing indeed. But how far down the scale of sizes intermittent breeding extends is not yet known. It stops short, as I have shown, of the Manx shearwater. It does not apply to the storm-petrel, for marked birds have returned year after year to the same crevices in the rocks and stone walls at Skokholm. The fulmar petrel is somewhat larger than the Manx

shearwater, but I am doubtful if it is so much an intermittent breeder as Wynne Edwards suggests. Wynne
Edwards based his belief partly on the discoveries mentioned above, and in particular on the fact that he obtained
'non-breeding' fulmars, with ovaries as described, at Cape
Chidley, Labrador, on 26th July, at a date when he reckoned
all breeding fulmars should be at their nesting grounds.
Cape Chidley is 400 miles south of the fulmar's nearest
breeding haunt.   In the next chapter I shall show that
400 miles is well within the feeding range of a Manx
shearwater breeding at Skokholm, and as the fulmar is
as powerful a flier as the Manx shearwater (it is in fact
more powerful), we can suppose that it has little difficulty in
flying to Cape Chidley and back (say in search of food) if
it wishes to in the course of a day.

But Wynne Edwards found that the breeding organs of
the Cape Chidley specimens were quite regressed, as if
they had not bred recently, perhaps not for a year. I am
not surprised. Breeding organs regress quickly once incubation begins. By 26th July fulmars would be feeding
young in Baffin Island, 400 miles north of Cape Chidley,
and their organs would be well regressed. It was the
wrong time of year to take specimens—it would have been
helpful to have had the organs of a breeding bird at Baffin
Island examined for comparison with the 'non-breeders'
of Cape Chidley.

Finally Wynne Edwards found that the 'non-breeders'
he examined were moulting, on 26th July. Well, a large
proportion of shearwaters from Skokholm at that date
would be moulting, not so much those still with chicks to
feed, but rather those which, having failed to hatch off
the egg or having (as we have seen) failed to retain the
egg in the face of burrowing and competition, and unable
to lay a second time in one season, start the next phase of
their yearly cycle, the moult. In this state they are of course
indistinguishable from the non-breeding birds with which
they will then associate on the sea. At least we may

reasonably suppose that, since the fulmar and the Manx shearwater start egg-laying about the same time, much the same thing happens in the case of the disappointed breeding fulmars, and that by the end of July a large number of these adults with regressed organs and moulting plumage will be at sea.

Forty per cent of the breeding Manx shearwaters (fifty per cent in the knoll colony) at Skokholm, as I have shown, have failed to hatch their chicks at that date in July and are at sea. In addition there are the true non-breeders, the first-year birds, adding roughly between ten and twenty per cent more to swell the flocks at sea. These figures more than cover the twenty per cent of the fulmar population which Wynne Edwards considers remain at sea during the summer. In addition we need to remember how far the breeding adult can wander in search of food, as I shall describe in the next chapter.

The question of the intermittent breeding of the fulmar can only be settled by extensive ringing. The fulmar is now rapidly spreading over the coasts of the British Isles. It has of late years paid many visits to Skokholm, though I have never seen it alight on our cliffs. When it does, and when it starts to breed, I shall hope to begin ringing. Meanwhile other observers might care to take up such a task where they have access to a colony. It may not be the pleasantest task, for the fulmar, when approached closely, fires at you a jet of thin oil from the stomach lining. This oil has an appalling stench, which clings tenaciously in spite of many washings. In the Faroe Islands the people boil their clothes in cow urine to get rid of fulmar stench. However, the observer who is anxious to ring fulmars in order to study them should be able to escape this recurring disaster. He might, like a knight of old, go to the ledges with a shield on which to receive the contents of the fulmar's stomach. When the bird has exhausted its supply of oil, it can be picked up with hands protected with thick waterproof gloves.

When I was climbing the great fulmar-haunted cliffs of the Faroes the islanders told me that the adult fulmars return to the cliff ledges in December, scarcely three months after the young birds have left. This fact seems to fit in with the theory, expressed by Wynne Edwards, that the fulmars which return in one season are not those that were breeding there the previous summer. It may be so with the fulmar, but, as we have seen, it is not the case with the Manx shearwater. Caroline, for instance, had not once missed breeding in the ten years 1929–38. And the other villagers of the knoll returned year after year until they vanished altogether and were written down as 'missing, presumed dead.'

Certainly the fulmar, by its appearance so early as December at the cliffs, has not had much time, after the end of rearing duties in August and perhaps early September, to get through the annual moult and be in courting trim by December. The Manx shearwater, finishing with the land at about the same time, has a longer, more decent interval before reappearing in February. It is probably true that the unsuccessful breeders of last year are the first to appear in the spring, because they have had a longer time to rest and revive. But I have not been able to gather any firm evidence about this.

I wonder in what state of plumage the fulmars are when they arrive at the ledges in December? That ought to be investigated too. Most of the shearwaters on arrival at Skokholm in February and examined by me or submitted to H. F. Witherby have been in perfect feather, no sign of moult, seldom even the trace of a sheath. The exceptions have had a certain amount of moult on the head, neck, and throat, and with one or two old feathers on the body. Witherby, writing of the skins he has handled, states that he considers the moult may start a little in July and is generally over by February, but it may exceptionally last into April. So it is evident that the shearwater is usually in good feather when it responds to the impulse to visit the breeding ground.   In any case, if it is not fully moulted then the shearwater still has three (and the fulmar five) months at the breeding site before laying actually takes place.   This should allow the tardiest bird to complete its moult.

I have seen guillemots still in winter plumage (so conspicuous in the guillemot) at the nesting ledges as late as June.   The guillemot, like the fulmar, pays visits to the breeding cliffs in December.   Yet it is essentially an annual breeder.   The same can be said of the herring-gull, which, after feeding young as late as October, is back at the nesting terraces on the first fine day in November.

Intermittent breeding among the smaller sea-birds is not yet proved.   We should keep an open mind about it. Ringing, ringing, and more ringing—that is the only way in which we shall understand the individual bird and its wonderful life history.

I

CHAPTER XI

MIGRATION

So far, in ten chapters, I have only managed to say a little concerning the shearwater at its breeding ground, to relate my experiences with the bird on one small island. We have explored, and even sailed around, but we have not yet ventured out of sight of, Skokholm. Yet at the break of each day the shearwaters have flown from the island, and vanished far out into the ocean.

Where do they go?

Where, too, do the young birds swim—for you will remember that they cannot fly at first—when, deserted by their parents in the autumn, they leave the island and paddle so earnestly alone towards the empty horizon?

Will the books help us? Let us sum up the information there:

The Manx shearwater breeds chiefly on islands and headlands in Scotland, Ireland, Wales, and the Scilly Isles. There are also small colonies in the Faroes and Iceland, while eggs and young have been taken in Brittany, Madeira, and the Bermudas. In winter there is some migration southwards, but the extent of this is not known. While there are records of this species having been taken off the Brazilian coast, many remain in home waters all the year round. Common in the North Sea, though there is no breeding place on the east coast.

Some in the North Sea and others at the same moment off the coast of Brazil! A wide range! But possibly those off Brazil come from the Bermudas and not from the British Isles. It is only an assumption, but a reasonable one, that these North American birds, breeding in these warm islands of the Gulf Stream, more likely wander south to the hot equatorial waters of Brazil, and that the British breeding birds, reared in the cooler waters of Northern Europe, remain in a temperate latitude.   However nothing is proven of individual migration.   We know that the great shear-water, breeding at Tristan da Cunha, halfway between Cape Horn and the Cape of Good Hope, crosses the equator before the southern winter begins and so lives in perpetual summer, following that season as far north as Greenland, many thousands of miles away from Tristan.   Distance is no bar to this large cousin of our Manx shearwater; and the Manx shearwater, being but a smaller pattern of the breed, might very well be a great annihilator of distances, too.

But I wanted facts about individuals, not general informa-tion.   I wanted to discover the whole truth about the winter wanderings of Adam, Caroline, and Hoofti.   They sailed out into the ocean each autumn, and in the spring some returned and others did not.   So many, especially the very young and the aged, were killed by storms.   After very severe equinoctial storms the mainland shore of Pembrokeshire in the autumn occasionally receives thou-sands of the drowned bodies of young shearwaters and gannets which have been unable to fight clear of the rocks in time.   Storms and other misfortunes must overtake migrating shearwaters wherever they are, I supposed, and in the course of years, some of my ringed villagers from the knoll might be reported from abroad.

This was a forlorn hope, I knew.   I ringed compara-tively few in the village, and the rings did not last more than two years.   I could not reckon on these villagers for the information on migration which I required.   No; only by ringing several hundreds would I get results. The percentage of recoveries of all birds ringed by various workers and organizations in Europe (including the British Isles) is very low, averaging under three per cent.   But some species yield only fractional percentages.   No shear-waters marked in the British Isles had ever been recovered abroad.   But then hardly any shearwaters had been marked.

It remained therefore to ring shearwaters in the largest possible numbers. This I began to do in 1933. Rings, however, are an expensive item, costing three-farthings each, or six shillings a hundred. It is, I am told, the stamping of the inscription and the cost of keeping records and dealing with the correspondence arising out of recoveries both at home and abroad, that makes the rings so expensive. I wished, but could not afford, to ring thousands of shearwaters. Others fortunately came forward, men and women eager to see our shearwaters and to ring them personally, and it has lately been possible to mark in this way three to four thousand shearwaters every year at Skokholm.

I have referred to the difficulty of the rings wearing off in two years. To overcome this the makers began at my request to experiment with thicker rings and with various alloys and coatings. These experimental rings I tested one after another upon our shearwaters. They were an improvement, extending in most cases the life and legibility of the ring to three years. At the moment a still further improved ring is in use, one with duplicated inscriptions and long enough for one inscription to be protected by an overlap bearing the second inscription. Thus if the outer inscription wears off the inner one remains perfectly legible as long as the ring holds together. These rings may, it is hoped, last at least four years, thus extending the time during which the bird can be identified if recovered abroad, or for that matter at home.

During the years of our occupation of Skokholm up to the end of 1939, 17,761 shearwaters have been ringed there. But the major portion—15,319—has been ringed in the years 1936-9. Results are slowly coming in.

The first British-ringed shearwater ever to be recovered abroad was RS 2294, an individual first ringed in the knoll colony on 1st April, 1933. This bird had been one of the newcomers in that crowded year, had wandered about from home to home, now with one friend, now with another. But he had had no success with a mate. His last recorded appearance was on 10th May alone in Burrow M. (On 13th May this burrow was occupied by an old-established pair, a female ringed in 1930 and her mate, a 1931-ringed male. Both these birds died out of the colony before 1936.) On 28th August 1933 RS 2294 was shot by a French fisherman about three miles south-west of the lighthouse at Saint-Nazaire, in the mouth of the Loire. This was not entirely unexpected. The place was not more than 300 miles south of Skokholm. One felt that the shearwater, its summer duties done—and this was undoubtedly a young bird with nothing to do early in the autumn, with nothing more behind him than a vain flirtation—would naturally wander south, to undergo the next little crisis in its annual cycle, the moult, in the Indian summer of Biscay. And so, feeding on the sprats and small fry off the coast of Loire Inférieure, it had met its fate at the hands of a fisherman.

The sailor had found a ring on the bird's leg, and had shown it to the captain of his smack. He, thinking perhaps there might be a reward attached to the finding, had shown it to the authorities at Saint-Nazaire. It had eventually come to the desk of the mayor, who, quite impressed by the inscription, had sat down in his office overlooking the sea. . . . The mayor had taken up his pen to write a letter to the address on the ring, a letter of great cordiality, a letter written with pretty flourishes of the pen to emphasize certain stereotyped but none the less felicitous greetings with which he began and ended the communication. . . .

In due course the mayor, the authorities, the captain, the man with the gun, the whole of Saint-Nazaire, learned that the ring had been put on the shearwater, the black and white sea-skimmer, on a small island in the north, called Skokholm (what a strange name!), off *Le Pays de Galles*. . . . So that was where these sea-skimmers were nesting, eh? A pity they did not nest nearer Saint-Nazaire, at Belle-Île perhaps, or Île de Noirmoutier, or one of the small islands within sight, on a clear day, of Saint-Nazaire. There were even some sailors who had seen Skokholm. On reference to the charts they said they had been north and fished by the shoals around that coast, in the little Breton smacks which made money at the crayfish, the *langouste*. But the captain and the sailor with the gun were secretly disappointed; they received no reward beyond the slight pleasure of boasting about the event over their country wine. (No reward, indeed, is possible under a ringing scheme which is without Government support or subsidy and which is barely able to sustain itself, let alone pay rewards. And anyway, a system of rewards might encourage the shooting of harmless birds.) The ringing scheme was the richer for the knowledge, however, if the worse by several twopenny-ha'penny stamps. While the mayor of Saint-Nazaire had another good tale to tell at the mayoral table, and no one the poorer except the municipal treasury by some note-paper and stamps.

The second knoll villager to distinguish himself in like manner was RV 7507. I had ringed this bird on 13th August 1934—it had arrived that night like a bolt from the blue. It had been a cool night of NNW. wind and no moon, one of the last dark nights of August in which adults would be able to visit the island. The season was nearly at an end, the wood-sage and the heather were in full bloom, and we were already ringing young shearwaters in the knoll homes. RV 7507 may have been an accidental visitor, blown into the streets of the knoll by a trick of the wind. I prefer to believe, however, that he or she was a young bird, probably born in 1933 or even 1932, who was exploring the ground with an eye to the future, hunting out a desirable residence. But since he was killed abroad we shall never know the truth of this matter.

He was killed on 31st March of the next year (1935) by a Spanish fisherman who fired spreading shot into a flock of shearwaters in the sea off Lequeitio, near Bilbao, in the Basque country of northern Spain. The fisherman opened the stomachs of all the sea-birds he shot, so that he might find out what fish they had been feeding on. He would then set—or not set—his nets accordingly. Like the Breton, the Basque fisherman thought there might be a reward; at any rate it was interesting, the ring must not be thrown away idly. He carried the dead bird home. The event was discussed over the garlic and fish and wine. The shearwater would be skinned and eaten. The ring, luckily for me, was not put with the other curios in the jug in the cabinet containing wedding and family heirlooms. It was recognized that the inscription on it was English—was not the address London? So the fisherman himself took it to H.B.M. Consul at Bilbao next time his boat sailed there with fish. It was in safe hands then. If the fisherman got little satisfaction out of hearing for the first time of the existence of Skokholm, I at least got my reward in fresh knowledge of the extent of the migrations of my shearwaters.

If it was sad to think that the would-be villager of the knoll could return no more, at least he had not died in vain. He had carried the torch of the light on migration three hundred miles farther south across the Bay of Biscay. He was an important figure in my records; indeed, had it been easy to do, I should have given him a gilt-edged card in my files, so that I might, on demand, the more easily pick out his brief but very important history. And he had achieved a form of immortality, remote and obscure perhaps, by a similar record entered in the schedules which I returned to the British Museum each year.

The date of this second recovery abroad was interesting. By 31st March of any year adult shearwaters have taken possession of the knoll, and are spring-cleaning, and many are mated and have lined the nest. Yet here was one postulant for village life wandering in blue Basque waters when he should have been up in the greener waters of St George's Channel, early and ready to enter the knoll and to begin the struggle to win a mate and a burrow there. What was he doing then, six hundred miles from home? It was impossible to believe that he was on a day visit from Skokholm, for that would argue a cruise of 1,200 miles altogether, or fifty miles an hour for twenty-four hours! Yes, quite impossible!

I decided that RV 7507 had been too young to take the domestic life seriously. Some late impulse had made him explore the knoll in the second August of his life, when he was just beyond a year old. In March 1935, approaching his second birthday, he was still too young to return, his breeding organs as yet slow to develop. No, he was in no hurry to return to Skokholm. No doubt, if the Basque fisherman had fired into another part of the flock, RV 7507, having escaped this death, would have got back to the knoll eventually, perhaps in April or May. No doubt the whole flock off Lequeitio on 31st March had consisted of sexually immature individuals.

But more evidence to support this theory turned up. Among those who came forward to ring shearwaters was C. Wontner-Smith. Working in the honeycomb at the Head he ringed 1,618 adult shearwaters during mid July 1934. It was rather disheartening to think that, by 1937 at latest, all these rings would have worn off and fallen away from the legs of the shearwaters he had marked; but nevertheless the work had its reward in time. During the next year and a half there were eight recoveries abroad.

First, on an unspecified date in March 1935 one of these (Head burrow) birds was taken by a fisherman off Belle-Île in southern Brittany, not far north of the Saint-Nazaire recovery. Then on 8th April two were taken at sea off Mundaca—again in the Basque country not far from Bilbao. Two days later two were shot by French fishermen at Saint-Jean-de-Luz on the border of Spain. All these recoveries fitted in with my theory that shearwaters found abroad at this time of the spring were sexually immature and very likely non-breeders for that year.

Even when a sixth bird was recovered so late as 9th May at sea near Saint-Jean-de-Luz (the third in this place), I was not disturbed. I wrote a paper in the periodical *British Birds*, setting out my view, using the evidence provided by these ringed birds. I stated, what I honestly believed then, that I thought Wontner-Smith in ringing so many birds in July had probably picked up a great many 'non-breeders' which in that month and later frequent the island on suitable nights. I quoted the case of RV 7507 as an example of a non-breeder in the knoll colony which was later recovered abroad, in the early spring. These non-breeders, I said, are particularly easy to catch and ring as they sit about on the ground. They make little attempt to enter holes for the good reason that most of the holes are already occupied by breeding adults hatching or feeding young. I quoted the evidence of H. F. Witherby, to whom I had submitted two of these non-breeders which I had found billing and cooing in a shallow hole one midsummer night. He had found them to be a pair, but their breeding organs were quite small and undeveloped, and the oviduct of the female was thin and straight and had no doubt never passed an egg.

Another of Wontner-Smith's birds was recovered on 23rd April 1935 at sea off Ushant Island, the most westerly point of Brittany. This bird, I reckoned, had obviously been on its way north to Skokholm when shot. It had got nearer home than the bird of 9th May (Saint-Jean-de-Luz) because it was probably more mature, perhaps a year older.

Wontner-Smith's last recovery was taken on 9th September 1935 at Comillas, near Santander, forty miles west of Bilbao. This report was perfectly in order; it fitted the evidence of a movement south to the Bay of Biscay in the autumn. The bird had merely broken a little fresh ground; to be precise, forty miles more to the west than the previous record.

After this I had no occasion to revise my view that any Skokholm shearwaters found in April and May in the south of the Bay of Biscay must be sexually immature; at least not until something occurred to enforce a revision, as I

shall presently relate. From the continued extensive ringing of adults each year other recoveries came in to help us
to map out the range of Skokholm shearwaters at sea.
Thus three adults were recovered on Cornish shores in
July, washed ashore dead after some accident at sea. One
ringed on 5th July was picked up at Hartland Point, Devon,
eight days later. Six were recovered on the coast of
Finistère, the most westerly department of Brittany, in
April, July, August, and September.

One of these was recovered in a curious way. The bare
ring which had been put on a shearwater on 4th June 1937
was recovered on 12th April 1938 in the stomach of an
angler-fish. The angler-fish had been caught by a fisherman
using a ground line from the pier at Douarnenez; the fish
weighed 40 pounds. Exactly how the ring entered the
stomach of the angler-fish must remain a matter of opinion.
An angler-fish of that weight is large and voracious enough
to swallow, with its enormous gape, a fish half its weight
or more; so that it is possible that a smaller fish, a surface-
swimmer perhaps, attracted by the bird's pale leg with its
bright ring, had bitten the leg and ring clean off, swallowed
them, and then in turn had been swallowed by the angler-
fish. It is not altogether easy to suppose that the angler-
fish swallowed the shearwater direct because an angler-fish
dwells on the bottom of the sea—and dead shearwaters
do not sink. Nevertheless, the shearwater may have been
seized when making a specially low dive after food, even
perhaps when making a snap at the bony protuberances
which hang so cunningly as bait before the opened cavern
of the angler-fish's mouth. It is also said that the angler-
fish may rise to the surface occasionally at night; if so, here
would be another opportunity to swallow the shearwater.

I incline to the theory that the shearwater's leg and ring
were first snapped off by a smaller fish as the bird swam
at the surface. And I think so because a fair percentage of
our Skokholm shearwaters have mutilated feet, neat slices
cut out of the webs of one foot, or perhaps the three toes

cut off near the first joint, often the toes of one foot completely missing, and more rarely a leg itself severed close to the 'thigh' (where the feathers begin). Such mutilation —no raggedness, but sharp clean bites—can only be the work of fish.

To return to the evidence of migration. None of our adult, or for that matter young, shearwaters were recorded from beyond the Bay of Biscay. One adult, ringed at Skokholm on 7th June, was killed on 8th August of the same year at Quiberon, Morbihan. Another, ringed on 17th July, was recovered at Lorient, Morbihan, on 12th May of the following spring.

But the next recovery was revolutionary. A shearwater ringed at Skokholm on 15th April 1938 as an active breeder was reported from near Bordeaux on 5th June of the same year! There had been a heavy storm and it had been washed up next day on the outer coast at Lacanau-Océan.

This bird had started breeding at Skokholm in April. In June it was 500 miles away!

I remembered very well that we had had a terrible northerly gale sweeping the island on 1st and 2nd June, blowing the rain under the slates on the steep roof of the island house as never before. The crops in the garden had been scorched up. An empty 500-gallon water tank had danced away up hill and down dale across the island for a quarter of a mile before the hearty kicks of this wild wind. Even so, could *any* wind have driven the bird so far south? Moreover, it had been fine and calm on the 3rd, with southerly winds up to the 6th. But in the absence of more evidence I began to believe that this shearwater had been driven all the way, had flown 500 miles before the wind until, exhausted, it had collapsed on the sandy pine-clad shore of Gironde. After all, lapwings have been blown across the Atlantic from Ireland to Newfoundland in a strong SE. gale; a ring on one of these lapwings recovered in America had proved it a British-born bird.

I was still unwilling to believe that a shearwater breeding at Skokholm could also be feeding in the Bay of Biscay in the same season.

Another shearwater, ringed in June 1937 and recovered at Biarritz (Basses-Pyrénées) on 28th February 1939, was evidence only that Biscay was, more positively than we had realized, the winter haunt of our shearwaters. The report came to me that this bird had been—for once—caught alive and released again, a small mercy for which I was especially glad, for this was a bird ringed quite near the knoll, and with luck I might meet it again at Skokholm.

Then in May and June 1939 came half a dozen recoveries that settled once and for all the truth that our shearwaters are feeding in the farthest corners of the Bay of Biscay at the same time as they have nests and eggs at Skokholm—that they are, in short, flying distances of 600 miles to feed.

They are, of course, not necessarily flying the double journey of 1,200 miles in twenty-four hours. Apart from the physical difficulty of their doing so we have already seen that the shearwater does not need to return home every night. It performs its domestic duties, even its pre-egg or love affairs, in shifts of two and three days at a time. The days of fasting and working at home are interspaced with days of feasting and holidaying at sea. The shearwater is fussy about his midnight hours on land, but not about his days at sea. Imagine how pleasant it must be for him or her to say, after a spell of three to six days on the egg: 'And now for a good stretch and a feed. In half a day I'll be in warm Basque waters, among the sardines. Eureka!' And with a scream—not, indeed, at all unlike 'Eureka'—he runs into the breeze until it lifts his wings and carries him off into the dark void between the sea and the night sky.

Some such a thought, but less fanciful and merely a dim mental process, must be the driving force that sends the shearwater on a long run to Biscay. I do not suggest that Skokholm shearwaters feed nowhere else but in the

Bay of Biscay. I have seen them feeding much nearer
home, within a few score yards of Skokholm's red cliffs.
But that some do feed in Basque waters, among the ever-
plentiful sardines, here is the evidence from the nets and
guns of Basque and Pyrenean fishermen.

I take the witnesses one by one.

AT 234. Ringed at Skokholm on 7th May 1939, it
was taken at sea off Lequeitio, North Spain, seven days
later. This is perhaps our leading witness.

RX 4847. Very important witness, because it was first
ringed on 29th April 1937. Recovered at Skokholm
19th May 1938 and re-ringed 304499. Recovered at Skokholm again on 25th April 1939. Reported killed during
early May 1939 off the coast of Landes. Ring now in the
possession of the curator of Biarritz Museum. This bird
was at least four years old when killed, and was a tried
breeder at Skokholm.

300280. Ringed 4th August 1937. May have been
immature in that year, but was probably breeding in 1938,
and certainly in 1939. Recovered off Saint-Jean-de-Luz,
Basses-Pyrénées, on 16th May 1939. An excellent witness.

303401. Ringed 11th April 1938, and therefore almost
certainly a breeder in that year. Recovered off Lequeitio,
North Spain, on an unspecified date in May 1939. A
valuable witness.

305525. Ringed 18th July 1938. Recovered near Biarritz, 12th May 1939. This type of recovery, of which
examples have been given earlier in this chapter, can now
be regarded as corroborative evidence.

306709. Ringed 24th July 1938. Recovered 10th June
1939 at Biarritz.

308092. This has just come to hand. The bird was
ringed on 30th July 1938, and recovered on 8th April
1940, at Hendaye, Basses-Pyrénées.

We could also go back over most of the earlier quoted
records and armed with our new knowledge find further
evidence in birds taken during April and May and June off

this Basque-Pyrenean coast, evidence not necessarily refuting my first theory that these early recoveries were sexually undeveloped birds. Some of these may well have been non-breeders. But the important discovery has emerged from the more recent records just quoted; we have proved that the breeding shearwater may wander 600 miles from its burrow on Skokholm as well in the summer as at any other season. And these recoveries for the present certainly, and perhaps for always, have proved that the range of Skokholm shearwaters is limited to a quite narrow belt covering the Bristol and St George's Channels, the English Channel, and the Bay of Biscay.

It is rather astonishing that none of our shearwaters have been recovered north of Skokholm, or in the North Sea, where many Manx shearwaters have been observed at all seasons. But this evidence of the limitation of migration, coming as the reward of a long and tenacious study, is exciting. And as I began to reflect on this elucidation of the shearwater's movements at sea I recognized that thus are subspecies or local races of a species made. Through travelling within a wheel 600 miles in diameter the Skokholm shearwater, because it never seemed to leave that wheel, was essentially conservative. While, by clinging to a certain island or group of islands as well as to this fixed hereditary migration-route, it isolated itself still further. Isolation tends to develop special characteristics, until new species appear. It remains to be seen, if ever a similar study of shearwaters in Scotland, Ireland, or the Faroes be undertaken, whether ringing will prove a similar limited compass of movement and migration. It seems likely. It may well be that the shearwaters which fill the North Sea are birds from Scotland and farther north.

The taxonomists and morphologists and bird-skinners among us have found pleasure and work in separating the Manx or medium shearwater of Atlantic Europe from the medium shearwater which inhabits the Bermudas; but whether they are right in doing so I am no judge. They have—and quite rightly in this case, for the distinctions are clear and permanent—separated the Manx shearwater from the Mediterranean medium shearwater. And they have, in turn, divided the Mediterranean medium shearwater into eastern and western subspecies. So it is even possible that in time the medium shearwater inhabiting the Faroes and Iceland may receive the dignity of a new subspecific name and be separated from *Puffinus puffinus puffinus*, our Manx shearwater. How long such a separation will last will depend on how well the case is made out; subspecies have appeared and disappeared before now in the jaw-cracking tomes of the three-word taxonomist or trinomialist, or, as the field-worker vulgarly calls him, the splitter, to distinguish him from the lumper, the binomialist, who prefers to simplify his science by lumping all subspecies and variations under the double, the specific, title. I pretend to little or no knowledge of this branch of ornithology, which is the product of musty indoor research among bird-skins and books. Nevertheless I do not wish to sneer at taxonomy as some students do. Let me admit my ignorance and admit, too, that while I can smile at its excesses I can admire its successes, and I am grateful for its guidance. Linnaeus, the greatest field worker of his day, was also the greatest taxonomist.

In order to feed in the Bay of Biscay shearwaters breeding in the north of Scotland and in the Faroes would have to fly about twice as far from home as do our Skokholm birds. So it may well be that they do not visit there, at least in the breeding season, but form, instead, their own feeding grounds farther south. In this divergence, if it exists, they are therefore already distinct from ours. They are more certainly distinct by their breeding in a more northerly climate, in a summer season of long days and short nights. One wonders what cumulative effect the shorter night has had upon the Manx shearwaters of the Faroes and Iceland? But I shall say more on this presently, for in due course my inquisitiveness sent me to inspect these northern colonies.

So far the shearwater of the north, of Iceland, the Faroes, and Scotland, appears to be identical with our shearwater at Skokholm, and with the bird that breeds in Ireland and the Scilly Isles.

We need not scorn the idea of their ever being separated in our time, however. We have only to remember how the guillemot inhabiting the British Isles has been separated into two perfectly good races. On Skokholm the guillemot has a rich chocolate-brown mantle. In the Shetlands the guillemot has a back as black as that of the razorbill. So the distinction is very clear. It could only come about by isolation of the two races as breeding units. Curiously enough another variation in the guillemot, although also a geographical one, is shared by both the light- and dark-mantled races—I refer to the bridle or white ring around the eye which stretches, like the shaft or rest of a spectacle, towards the hidden ear. This is a feature which increases in frequency with the increase in latitude. We found none bridled in Portugal, the most southerly breeding ground of this guillemot. But at Skokholm ·5 per cent of guillemots are bridled, that is to say about one in two hundred. In the Faroes I reckoned about 40 per cent were bridled, while in the Westmann Islands of Iceland some 75 per cent were seen to be bridled. An inquiry conducted by H. N. Southern has confirmed this interesting geographical distribution, this gradual increase of bridling with increase of latitude. Thus, to fill in gaps in our own observations, in the Hebrides the percentage of bridled birds is 15, in the Shetlands 25. So that while we regard the bridled guillemot at Skokholm as abnormal, almost a freak, in Iceland it is the plain guillemot that appears to be an aberration. With us a bridled guillemot is so rare that it could not easily find another to mate with. I make this point in order to deny that a bridled guillemot deliberately seeks out another bridled bird to mate with. It does not. Bridled birds on Skokholm have always had plain mates. Bridling does not make a new race, it is

A flashlight photograph of a Mousonal, monton laine almost in laine...

not a fixed character; it is rather a Mendelian variety, like
red hair in human beings. The two races of the guillemot,
the northern and southern, have their different percentages
of bridling; but so, too, have the races of man their different
percentages of red-haired persons.

The British razorbill is the latest sea-bird victim of the
splitter. The trinomialist has added the subspecific *Britan-
nica* to the Linnaean *Alca torda*, and has given certain fine
plumage distinctions as reasons which may or may not
appear increasingly to be adequate.

To return to the shearwater, and in particular the Skokholm bird which as a subspecies is as yet only recognizable
by its habit of breeding on Skokholm and migrating as far
south as the Bay of Biscay, a subspecific character which
even the most confirmed splitter would hesitate to seize
upon. If our shearwaters fly south to Biscay to feed,
during the early summer, as ringing would indicate, a tide
of migrating birds should at that season converge into a
concentrated stream off those points of the coast which
lie across and intercept a line drawn from Skokholm to the
Bay of Biscay. Such a line cuts across the leg of Cornwall
and the arm of Brittany. Therefore we should meet with
shearwaters off Land's End and Ushant. What news is
there of such a migration?

There are several records of shearwaters flying in numbers
past Land's End. On 2nd June 1924 H. M. Wallis records
'a continuous movement of shearwaters going from north-
west to south-east off Land's End, about 150 to 200 counted.'
(*British Birds*, xviii. 74). At noon on 14th April 1929
150 a minute were passing east to west across Mount's
Bay, Cornwall, before a strong south-east wind (*British
Birds*, xxiii. 20). W. H. Thorpe records numbers flying
south from Cape Cornwall in April 1935; in three hours
during the middle of the day shearwaters passed at the rate
of 240 a minute (equal to 43,200!). The movement greatly
subsided by 6 p.m. On 12th April an hour's count gave
1,460 shearwaters, 600 auks, 158 gannets; wind being fresh

K

from the north-east. On the 13th, shearwaters were passing
in the morning at the rate of 400 an hour (*British Birds*,
xxix. 43). P. H. T. Hartley saw similar movements
during the Easter and summer vacations, 1932–5. He
counted 20,000 shearwaters passing in a single morning,
the movement being south-west past Zennor and Gurnard's
Head towards Cape Cornwall and then south-west to the
west of the Longships. There was also some movement
west-south-west from Mount's Bay, past Lamorna and out
for the Scillies. On 25th August 1933 he records shearwaters moving south over an area at sea some miles west
of the Longships. He has only one record in four years
of northward movement (six birds on 25th August 1933),
and all shearwaters were moving in the morning, none
after 6 p.m. He adds that all movements were intensified
in heavy weather. (*British Birds*, xxix. 203.)

Bertram Lloyd, in commenting on the above records,
says that these movements, and others he has observed off
Wales, south-east Ireland, and the Scillies, are associated
entirely with feeding. (*British Birds*, xxix. 260). Our
ringing work proves that this keen observer is right in his
bold assertion.

We are, however, somewhat puzzled that there should be
so little evidence of the return movement to the islands
of Pembrokeshire. Obviously the birds must return at
some time. If heavy weather presses the tide of southward-
bound birds against the promontories of Cornwall, just as
the movements of the sea intensify the currents at the
headlands of Skokholm, then the rush of northward-bound
birds should likewise be forced against the coast. Pending
a better observation of Cornish and Breton headlands we
must be content to suppose that the northward, the return,
movement is more leisurely and on a wider front than the
southward trek. I myself have seen very large flocks
flying north from Lundy across the Bristol Channel to
south Pembrokeshire and Skokholm during the latter half
of the day. I have also seen smaller flocks converging

on Skomer and Skokholm from the north, from Cardigan Bay. From the west, from the wide ocean, arrivals are less in evidence; coming home from Grassholm in the evening, after a day with the gannets, we see only single birds, or two and three together, making east with us.

CHAPTER XII

THE YOUNG BIRD AT SEA

IN the course of eleven years Adam and Ada, Carol and
Caroline, and the other recorded but less important old-
timers and their successors, reared many young birds in
the village on the knoll. But although I ringed all these
as they approached desertion stage, I never recaptured a
shearwater born and reared and ringed in the knoll homes.
If they ever returned they did so long after their rings,
and with them their identity, had been lost.

In the six years 1929–34 I ringed 93 young birds in and
about the knoll. In the six years 1935–40 not one of the
93 was recovered, at Skokholm or elsewhere.

For the maintenance of the Skokholm race of shearwaters, and — what particularly interests us — for the
flourishing of the knoll colony, a yearly accession of young
blood replacing the old must come largely if not entirely from
shearwaters bred at Skokholm. That is to say, some time
or other, the majority of those youngsters that survive to
maturity must return to Skokholm to breed. If Hoofti
or Toofti had returned to the knoll in the summer following that of their exit as nestlings, I should assuredly have
met them. That they did not return helps me to believe
that the young bird does not breed at one year old, and
therefore has no occasion to visit the island—at least more
than spasmodically—in its second summer. But none of
the 93 marked in the home meadow returned there within
the time when their rings remained legible (2½ years).
Therefore, in addition to not breeding at a year old, it
seems likely that the young bird does not necessarily return
to the same burrow or group of burrows in which it was
born. Otherwise, let me repeat, I should surely have
recovered one or two out of the 93 youngsters.

Of course the young bird must eventually return to the island to breed; but when it did so it probably, I thought, flew widely over the breeding ground before selecting, and thereafter becoming familiar with, a suitable burrow. Incidentally this change of site is a natural safeguard against inbreeding.

We can surmise, further, that the young bird, in its first visits to the island, is encouraged by and carried along with the flocks of adults which, as dusk deepens to full night, rise from the sea and invade the island. The wild cries excite the novice bird—whose breeding organs are but slowly developing—and it, too, now gives out its first screams. At last, after flying to and fro above the ground, it crashes down boldly to make its first landing since it tumbled out of the egg. The youngster is *stimulated* to make its first landing by the presence of older birds. It is unlikely that it would have landed quite by itself on land not inhabited by Manx shearwaters.

This encouragement, this stimulation in numbers, is a new adaptation of the old adage of safety in numbers. Almost all kinds of life, from man to birds and plants, are known to thrive best when they have others of their species with or near them, especially in the breeding season. It is even suggested that there is a number, or numerical threshold, below which a sociable-nesting species does not, is not able to, breed with success. Two is of course the minimum number among warm-blooded animals, including birds. But the mere presence of another bird, not necessarily of the same sex, is known to provide a stimulus which acts on the pituitary, and thus encourages the cycle of breeding in a healthy bird.

So two or three pairs of a sociable species succeed better than one pair. This is actually true of the budgerigar in confinement. Fraser Darling has found that it may be applied in general to the sociable sea-birds. Darling found, for instance, that the largest colonies of gulls reared the most chicks per pair. And in my experience small colonies

of guillemots do not start visiting their nesting places, and
therefore do not start breeding so early, and do not breed
so successfully, as the larger loomeries. The stimulation
of numbers is working here. How far it is possible be fix
arbitrarily a numerical threshold for the various species
is doubtful. Darling gives the gannet as a typical instance
where the stimulation provided by the group is essential
to the completion of the breeding cycle in this closely
gregarious species; but in fact an isolated pair of gannets
has recently bred successfully in a new site on Great Saltee
Island, Co. Wexford. Nevertheless the presence of numbers
is very important in stimulating the breeding cycle. Man
himself is no exception—the excitement and hysteria of
crowds and mobs in towns are well known. And so with
the shearwater, especially the young shearwater. Hoofti
and Toofti, adolescents in the crowd of adults, are probably
as excited as any young persons at a cinema, a jamboree,
or a dance.

Accepting the view that the larger the group the greater
the stimulation and the greater the success in breeding, it
will be apparent that the crowded colonies of shearwaters
at the Head and the western end of Skokholm succeed, in
spite of the seeming confusion, in rearing a larger percentage
of young per head of adult population than the smaller
colonies do. We have seen that there were many tragedies
in the knoll colony during incubation. I have already
stated that only fifty per cent of the eggs hatched. On
the other hand, when the village was most crowded, the
disasters seemed to be most frequent. And over the whole
eleven years of my vigil the village continued to flourish
equally with the slums at the Head; the numbers in each
appeared to be controlled only by the number of desirable
residences available—each year every decent burrow was
tenanted.

As I have already suggested that the adolescent shearwaters, on first making the island, are guided by the mass-
uproar and excitement of the adults, it may also be that

this brings them first to the metropolis at the Head. Later, if they fail to secure a breeding burrow there in the face of the obviously severe competition, they are perhaps compelled to move to the outskirts of the town. Even here there is competition. They must move farther and farther out until a home is secured. This would imply a relation between population and distance from the town—as is the case with *Homo sapiens*. In point of fact this ratio obtains, somewhat roughly, at Skokholm; it might be said that there is an urban, a suburban, and a country shearwater population. We might name these, according to their respective positions on the island: west, near-west, and east. The nature of the ground, however, is a controlling factor. Where the soil is easy to burrow small townships and large villages have grown up in the country. But in general the number of shearwaters in the extreme northeast of the island is small; the burrows there are largely occupied by rabbits and puffins. But as you return to the Head on a dark night the numbers of shearwaters and the noise increase with every step, and you have the feeling that you are coming to town.

I wondered if the survivors of the 93 youngsters ringed in and near the knoll had returned to the island via the town at the Head. But, in any case, their rings were dropping away gradually, and as the years moved by my hope of recovering these young villagers diminished. In 1935 therefore I began ringing larger numbers of fledgelings. I worked chiefly in the centre of the town, near the lighthouse, because the downy chicks were most numerous there. At night in late August and during September it was easy to catch them as they sat about, in the wing-exercising stage of desertion. And they were easy to identify by torch-light because of fringes and tufts of down clinging to their plumage.

In four autumns, 1935–8, with the help of visitors, we ringed 2,746 young shearwaters.

The first recovery was that of a fledgeling ringed on 6th

September 1936.   It was picked up only three days later
on the strand at Saint-Valery (Seine-Inf.) on the north coast
of France near Dieppe!   No doubt RX 4408 had been
blown ashore by the howling westerly gale which had
swooped down on the island on 7th September.   That
day had been so wild that even the trawlers, those little
ships manned by men who seem not to know any fear,
which plunge past Skokholm on their way to the fishing
grounds in all weathers, turned back and made for the
shelter of Milford Haven.

RX 4408 had probably started south on the night of
ringing—the night of 6th–7th.   It had started to blow then,
enough to fill the young bird's wings and enable it to fly
instead of flapping as on a calm night.   But it seems
unlikely that so young and inexperienced a bird succeeded
in making enough westing against the stiff south-west wind
that night to clear Land's End (120 miles to the south-
south-west) and by this route reach the English Channel
and Saint-Valery.   On the 7th there was nearly a whole gale
from north-west.   If we look at the map we shall see that
Skokholm lies approximately due north-west from Saint-
Valery, on a line which crosses Somerset and Dorset.
Is it possible that RX 4408, driven helplessly down wind on
the morning after the night it was ringed, was blown
clean across the land to the English Channel, and on reaching the sea was washed ashore at Saint-Valery?   I think this
is most likely; it is the only reasonable explanation in this
case.

Stranger abmigrations have occurred.   At the same time
as RX 4408 was blown ashore in France unusual migrants
reached Skokholm from other shores.   Tired Lapland
buntings (young birds, too) from Arctic shores were seen
and one was captured on the island.   Less accountably,
ortolans also appeared.   These could only have come from
their breeding grounds in an east or north-east direction,
but the Lapland buntings, breeding in Greenland, might
have been blown hither from the north-west.   Possibly

the ortolans, migrating southwards from Norway via the west coast of Britain, had been overtaken by the gale while north-west of Skokholm.

In the following year a young shearwater, ringed on 1st September, was picked up nine days later inland in Wales, in the colliery district of Tonyrefail, Glamorganshire. It, too, had obviously been blown out of its course. The weather during those ten days had been rough, with strong winds, chiefly from south-west and west, winds which accounted for the appearance of 300653 in a direction almost due east of Skokholm. It is also important to note that the young bird was able to fly so soon after fledging, no matter if it did fly in the wrong direction and inland. It assists us to believe that RX 4408 flew over Somerset and Dorset to France.

These early autumnal gales strike at a critical time in the life of the young shearwater. As we have seen, a strong wind is a great help in enabling the nestling to take off from the land, but a gale has its disadvantages on the sea. It raises broken water which the nestling, unable to fly for hours at a stretch, must face when it at last strikes the sea. The nearer inshore the inexperienced and exhausted bird drifts the heavier and more violent are the breakers, and the more difficult it is for the bird to swim clear.

September 1935 in the west was a month of storms, with a particularly severe gale from south-south-west on the 16th. On the 18th I walked for two miles along the mainland shore near Newgale, Pembrokeshire, from which the islands of Skokholm and Skomer lie approximately in a south-south-west direction. There were many birds washed ashore, dead. I counted 102 shearwaters (only one alive), 13 herring-gulls, 2 lesser black-backed gulls, 1 great black-backed gull, 1 kittiwake gull, 5 gannets, 3 razor-bills, and a puffin, nearly all juveniles. None of the birds had signs of oil, and all had evidently been driven ashore by stress of weather. None was ringed.

The late T. A. Coward, author of *Bird Haunts and Nature Memories*, believed that shearwaters migrated overland. In a letter to me, he pointed out the evidence: there was a large number of recoveries of shearwaters inland in England in early autumn. And he sent me a long list of the recoveries he had noted from journals and books. I argued, in my reply to him, that, as there was no similar evidence of an inland passage in the spring, i.e. no recoveries inland at that season, it was more than likely that the autumn records were merely those of storm-driven young birds. I suggested that the meteorological data for the days preceding each record should be tabulated and placed alongside his list. Coward promised to do this. In his last letter he was planning to stay with us and be introduced to the knoll colony. But a few days later this fine naturalist died suddenly.

W. E. Kenrick took on the work of placing the inland records beside the meteorological information. He found that there was a very full correlation. The recoveries ranged over a period from mid-August to mid-October (from 1839 to the present day), just the time when young shearwaters are leaving the islands. The days preceding almost each recovery were found to have been stormy, as a rule with some notable gale from a westerly quarter. Like the ringed bird that ended its existence at a colliery pit-head, these birds of Coward's were all storm-driven. The inland migration was disposed of.

So far there have been no further recoveries abroad of shearwaters ringed as nestlings at Skokholm. For the present we are at liberty to surmise that the juvenile shearwaters wander south to Biscay with the adults, to return again with them in the spring.

As I shall relate, ringing eventually told me that the juveniles visit the island in the spring, but almost certainly do not breed until they are at least 20 months old.

I was almost despairing of ever recovering at Skokholm a shearwater ringed there as a nestling, when at last one of a batch of 179 youngsters ringed in 1935 returned on 4th April 1937, seventeen months after it had left the island as a fledgeling. The date of its return was sufficiently early to suggest that it intended to breed in this its third summer, at nearly two years of age.

Of 624 nestling shearwaters ringed in 1936 one returned in August 1938, and a second in July 1939. The ring on the last, after three years' wear, was only just decipherable, and was hanging loose, ready to drop off.

Of 1,322 nestlings ringed in 1937 nine returned, two in July 1938 (immature birds exploring for the future? The late date suggests this); and seven in 1939, two of these on 15th June, the rest during July.

Of 621 nestlings ringed in 1938, four were recaught in 1939, one on 22nd April one on 15th June, and two during July.

The average return of nestlings to their place of birth is, if we are to judge from the four years' work, very low, a little more than one half of one per cent. But no great importance need be attached to this percentage. All these birds were ringed and recovered in the metropolis at the Head. Had I and others been able to spend more nights than we did at the Head, catching shearwaters, we could, I doubt not, have raised this percentage considerably. As it was, between other duties, we could not find time for more than occasional visits throughout the summer.

The April recovery in 1939, showing that a shearwater can return to the breeding ground within ten months of being hatched there, rather upsets my theory that the shearwater does not return to the nesting site until it is at least a year old. But if this bird did breed in 1939 it was exceptional, for we have already proved that young birds, found exploring the land at midsummer, are not breeding —they have almost completely undeveloped genital organs. However, this visit to land by 310373 so early in its life is not to be dismissed lightly. It deserves closer examination.

22nd April 1939 opened a brilliant day with a strong

north-west breeze against which a migration of swallows
and martins struggled northwards across the island, their
white breasts skimming low over the yellow primroses,
the white sea-campion, the first bluebells, and some early
sea-pinks. A peregrine falcon, which for days had been
attacking the small birds and the puffins, rose upon the
wind vertically, and climbing higher and higher, dwindled
and vanished against the infinite blue of the sun-filled sky.
Towards evening heavy rain clouds came up out of the
west and covered the setting of the young bow of the new
moon. The wind eased and the whole sky became suddenly dark. That night was black and starless and full of
shearwaters. When we reached the Head at 11 p.m. the
uproar was—well, it was stimulating even to my accustomed
ears. My friends tried to find the right superlatives to
describe it all. Shearwaters brushed past us, even hit us,
each shouting as if mad with the general excitement. We
could have ringed two thousand shearwaters with ease if
we had brought the rings and had sufficient help. As it
was the 40 rings which we had in our hands were quickly
used up. We went straight to the middle of the colony
and picked up the first birds to hand. Out of the first
44 birds picked up five were already ringed, four with
rings still strong and legible, but the fifth needed changing.
Of these five recoveries two were found, on reference to
the books, to be adults ringed in 1937, two were adults
ringed in 1938, and the last was 310373, ringed as a nestling
on 1st September 1938.

In that darkness, in that bedlam, in that honeycomb, it
was impossible to study the movements of individuals.
310373 was lost as soon as released. But I felt it was easy
to explain the presence of this young bird. It was easy
for me to imagine that, on this night of exceptionally
stimulating conditions, 310373, and probably other young
birds, had been swept up with the main flock gathered on
the sea in the evening, in the general invasion of the
metropolis. On brighter, less suitable nights, 310373, and

others drawn from his age-group, would not land, would not feel the stimulation and mass-excitement that drew them to make their first landings. They might be far away on those moonlit nights, even in Basque waters—along with the adult breeders from Skokholm, which, as we have seen, visited the Bay of Biscay throughout the egg-laying period from April to June.

*   *   *   *   *

The lot of the young bird in finding a home and a mate for the first time is, the reader will have gathered, not an easy one. From our study of the shearwater it is clear that the young bird has to face severe competition in the overcrowded conditions underground at Skokholm. It has, literally, to wedge and fight a way into an established colony; failing which it remains a homeless non-breeder.

It is now more than thirty years since Manx shearwaters received any serious persecution at the hands of man on the Pembrokeshire islands. Previously, farming operations had reduced the burrowing area on the islands, fishermen had collected shearwaters for baiting lobster pots, and there is even a record of shearwaters being ploughed into the ground for manure—at Skomer. But in thirty years of peace from human intervention the shearwater has rapidly increased. With the help of rabbits it has opened up new breeding colonies on the now unfarmed and almost derelict islands. It has, we can safely say, reached a climax state there—it can multiply no more without overflowing. Its natural enemies, the gulls and ravens and buzzards, have also increased, and are doing their best towards killing off the surplus shearwaters. This increase of predators may not necessarily be associated with the increase of shear-waters. Probably the great increase in rabbit populations throughout West Wales is mainly responsible, together with lack or stoppage of persecution by man, for this in-crease of these large birds. And the shearwaters flourish exceedingly in spite of large numbers of great black-backed gulls, and many ravens and buzzards, taking toll on the islands.

They flourish to the extent of overflowing in all directions. For some years Manx shearwaters have been making landings on dark nights on the mainland coast opposite their breeding islands. Ferreters, working in the cliffs at Marloes and Dale, have told me that they have found shearwaters in holes there. One reliable rabbit catcher declares he has found a bird sitting on an egg in a cliff overlooking Jack Sound and Skomer. I myself have often heard stray birds at night, as they flew screaming over the mainland coast, from St David's southwards to the Carmarthen border at Amroth. One misty spring night a shearwater crashed through a chapel window at Dale, during a service. I picked up another outside the door of a house in Dale.

Yet none of these seeming attempts at colonization of the mainland appears to have been successful so far. I am more concerned, in this chapter, to know which birds go forth to establish, or attempt to establish, new colonies —the young inexperienced shearwaters, or the old tried breeders?

It seems more probable that old breeders, having established themselves in warrens, remain there for the rest of their breeding lives. They are not concerned with finding new homes—the regularity with which the knoll inhabitants returned to their respective burrows each year tells us this plainly. It must be the young birds that are forced to establish new colonies.

Here again we come up with the theory of a numerical threshold which must be reached before successful breeding takes place. We see it working in another member of the tube-nosed family. It is now known that the fulmar petrel may haunt a new site for years before breeding takes place, and that breeding does not take place until a sufficient number of individuals are assembled at the new site. This has so far been true of the South Pembrokeshire cliffs, where for the last ten years from three to six pairs of fulmars have haunted a certain part without laying eggs—though they are to be seen sitting about and courting on the ledges. This appears to be an exceptionally long 'waiting' period, for in the same years fulmars have first visited, and then colonized and bred at, for instance, Saltee and Lambay Islands in Ireland. If the South Pembrokeshire fulmars are always the same birds and were immature at first they must be fully mature now, and their failure to breed is on a parallel with the failure of Manx shearwaters to establish themselves securely as breeders on the mainland.

A similar failure has come to my notice from accounts sent to me by visitors to Great Saltee Island, Ireland. For at least ten years, and probably earlier, shearwaters have been heard at night (as they have also on Lundy) at Great Saltee. But no eggs or chicks have been found there, in spite of intelligent searching. It is at midsummer that the shearwaters are noisiest. Writing to me of a visit in late July 1937, R. S. Pollard says that:

We had given up the idea that there was a breeding colony of shearwaters on Great Saltee, and accordingly we were not on the look-out for them. It was only the accident of my getting back very late on our last night but one that led to the discovery. It was very dark and we heard the birds calling about 11.30 p.m. We went down to the boat landing. Shearwaters were calling excitedly off-shore but also, it seemed to me, over the island. I decided to walk over on to the south side. I found numbers of birds landing there and the air was full of noise as far as the ear could reach. When I got my friends out of bed by showing them a shearwater I had captured on the ground, they were just as much impressed as I was with the numbers of birds landing. The next night was not so dark, but we found much the same thing happening. Many of the holes were in the sea-campion and the birds had to dive through a curtain of trailers into their holes. Others were squatting in the bracken patches or along the walls. We put rings on some of them and marked one or two holes. The following day we were due to leave, and we had rather bad luck with our marked holes, as several were too deep. But we dug down to one and were amazed to find two birds in a hole. Both these were in adult plumage, but one looked very young, with its webs strongly pigmented. The date is too early for a chick to be at that stage, but we couldn't find anything more convincing, and it seemed curious that two birds should be together if they were adult. There had been a great deal of noise in this hole the night before, but all very amicable. I ought to say, too, that there was a good deal of underground love-making all over this area. I should like to hear what you think about all this.

What I think about this account will be obvious to the reader of this book. I have already described how adolescent shearwaters visit unoccupied burrows and holes at midsummer, or sit about in the open. The same thing was happening at Great Saltee. The young appearance of one of the adults in the burrow fits in with my supposition that the age of most of these colonists is tender. The 'mate' of this bird might have been older, possibly a bird which had visited Great Saltee many seasons without breeding.

Thus we have a glimpse of a group of young colonists visiting an ideal site over several years, becoming thoroughly familiarized with the ground by repeated visits in the summer, gradually increasing in numbers, and arriving at the point of breeding. In due course we may expect to hear that the Manx shearwater is proved to breed at Great Saltee, Co. Wexford, Ireland. (The only possible drawback, I am told, is, as at Lundy Island, the presence of rats —but puffins breed successfully there, so perhaps shearwaters will, in the end.)

Mr. Puffin, who shares the island burrows with the shearwaters

CHAPTER XIII

HOMING EXPERIMENTS

On 6th June 1936 the biology master at Dartington Hall School pitched two bell-tents in the bracken in the home meadow. David Lack had with him, like an embodied enthusiasm, the bird-loving children of Bertrand Russell, Stephen Leacock, Clough Williams-Ellis, and others. There was some difficulty about placing the tents where they would do least interference to nesting birds and flowering plants —for which reason I was at first reluctant to permit camping at all. Fortunately the bluebells were nearly over, and the bracken did not matter, so the tents were pitched over a bed of bluebells and bracken, with care to avoid the shearwater burrows in the ground and the crevices in the old hedge-walls where storm-petrels nested.

The experiment had its reward for me in watching the eager happiness of these children as they scoured the island studying and discussing bird and flower, seal and rabbit and insect, the movement of the tides, the clouds, the wind, and the stars. And in the evening, when the driftwood fire would be lit in the hearth, the children would come tumbling into my house, to sit before the blue and yellow flames and speak of their adventures, their voices sharp with suppressed excitement. They all had something urgent to say, some important contribution to make to the day's records.

After the records had been entered up we would talk on into the dusk, a little solemnly perhaps, as do those who are young and met together by reason of a common love. We talked learnedly of birds, their courtships, their nesting, their migrations, their extraordinary homing powers. . . .

How does the young cuckoo find its way to Africa,

alone, late in the summer, long after its parents have flown south? How does the English swallow find its way back each year to its old nest on the rafter, after a winter spent in Cape Province? How does the great shearwater find its way back to Tristan da Cunha, that needle in the hay-stack of the Southern Atlantic, after six months of wander-ing in northern waters, about Greenland and in the Gulf Stream? What is the secret of homing? Do birds fly by sight, by a polarized sense, by a hereditary instinct, or by some wonderful sixth sense which man cannot fathom? Do birds fly at great heights on migration, and by some power, like that of the infra-red ray, see immense distances before them? If so, of what use is such sight to the young migrating bird that has never traversed the traditional migration path of its species? What could be done by way of experiment to elucidate this mysterious power of homing which almost all birds seemed to possess? Had any experiments been carried out recently? What had been done in the past?

Quite a lot of experimental work had been done in the past. Lashly and Watson had had some success with noddy and sooty terns returning from distances outside the known geographical range of these species. Riviere, working with homing pigeons, had reached the conclusion that these tame birds had a distinct 'sense of geographical position.' And I could tell the Dartington children of an experiment I had made with the help of the pigeon expert, Major W. H. Osman. Osman had sent me five young untrained pigeons from London lofts. I released them here (240 miles from London) on a fine sunny day with a light south-east wind and moderate visibility, on 26th May 1935. The object was to see if absolutely untrained young pigeons could return over such a distance. An east wind with slight haze, such as prevailed that day, has often proved too much for trained birds, and is reckoned about the worst flying weather for pigeons. None of the five returned. At the same moment my friend H. Morrey

Salmon had released four untrained pigeons (from London lofts also) at Cardiff, a hundred miles nearer London. One of these returned to its home loft in just over four days, i.e. working its way home at the rate of some 37 miles a day, which Osman reckoned to be a good performance for an untried bird. Only one other was recovered—one of the Cardiff-released pigeons turned up at West Bromwich. Thus only one out of the nine pigeons was proved to have a strong homing ability. It is interesting to note that none of the pigeons attempted to gain any great height on being released. Most of them flew very low, under 50 feet from the ground, including the successful homer; while two of the unsuccessful birds circled to 200 feet before vanishing.

It is doubtful if birds fly very high on their migrations. It is rare for the aviator to encounter birds above 20,000 feet. On this question it is worth while quoting a letter I received from an airman stationed in the south of England. He writes:

I was stationed near Chichester in Sussex for three years, during which time we used to climb and fly several times a week at heights from 20,000 to 30,000 feet. As you know, the Sussex coast is a good place for migrants making their entry to England, but at no time did we ever meet birds at heights of more than three or four thousand feet, and that rarely. In these isolated cases they were always a flock of peewits or an occasional gull. I have also encountered a cormorant at 1,500 feet over the Isle of Wight. This fellow was very intrepid, and though I had a 'dog-fight' with him for some five minutes he insisted on going on his course, when I left him alone. It is fairly certain that, just as with ourselves, birds would need oxygen were they to fly above 18,000 feet. As to the question of location of themselves when on their journeys, it remains to me as a pilot the most fascinating problem in the world. We had a pair of swallows nesting in the Mess porch year after year. We ourselves after flying over the sea for an hour or so would return by flying due north till we struck the coast and then turning west or east as the case may be, till we reached home. But even with the help of maps it took some years to recognize instantly any part in 150 miles of coastline. Yet unless we suppose some extra sense in these birds other than purely a north and south orientation, how can we explain their obvious knowledge of whether to turn east or west when they first strike the coast?   We could do it by having a compass giving us the north—which the birds may also sense, and also by our memory and a map.   But is it possible that a first-year swallow returning could distinguish, let us say, Bexhill from Worthing, and therefore know which way to turn?

Pilot F. H. Dixon concludes his interesting letter with a note on the debatable question of the homing instinct in man.   He writes:

There is a curious vestige of the homing sense in ourselves— it has been often commented on.   It is surprising how often, after a flight above 10/10th cloud, one has a strong instinct that the aerodrome lies just so.   And like other instincts, the first effort to analyse one's reason for so thinking upsets the original notion and all is lost.   I have read most of the theories of migrating location but find them so contradictory that one has to fall back upon the old homing instinct and leave it at that, especially as I am convinced we have a rudimentary trace left.

Well, could we discover something fresh about the homing power of the sea-bird?   It was Lack who, as we developed the discussion on homing, asked that the children should take back to Dartington with them some shear-waters.   These they would release at Start Point, the most southerly finger of Devon.   It would be interesting to learn if and how soon the birds would return to Skokholm.

When the party left us on 17th June they took with them—for the idea was irresistible and grew ambitiously— three shearwaters, three storm-petrels, and six puffins.

There was little doubt that the shearwaters would get home easily; they were grand fliers and would probably be first back.   On the day our visitors were leaving I selected the first three birds which happened to be incubating when I opened the trap-doors of the knoll homes: RV 7569, a bird which was first ringed in 1935, when it laid an egg in nest G; RS 2255, a grand old fellow first registered in 1931, who had contracted a bigamous marriage and of whose first wife, still living, we shall hear more presently; and AE 699, our invaluable Caroline.

I was to regret having sent RS 2255, for neither he nor RV 7569 returned. Lack wrote to say that, unaccountably, these two birds died in their crates while on the train between Pembrokeshire and Devon.

This was a blow; but at least Caroline, my most cherished and the oldest bird in the knoll, had managed the overland journey. Lack wrote that the surviving shearwater, in common with the puffins and the storm-petrels, flew directly out to sea when released from the cliffs of Start Point. They took no special line, and certainly did not fly directly for Skokholm, neither north-west over the land, nor west over the sea. They flew at right angles to the coast, as if anxious to put distance between them and the land—with, as I thought, its recent unpleasant associations of confinement in a quivering wooden crate.

Lack's letter with this information did not reach me for a few days—our post on the island being spasmodic. However, we had arranged that he was to release the birds some time on 18th June. Start Point is 225 miles from Skokholm by sea around Land's End. I anticipated that if the puffins and the storm-petrels flew at about 10 miles an hour surface speed, and the shearwaters at about 15 miles an hour, this would be a very good average rate of progress, having regard to natural deviation of flight and the necessity for rest and food *en route*. This speed could not bring them to Skokholm before daylight on the 19th, and so, I argued, it would hardly be worth while looking for the nocturnal birds, the petrels and shearwaters, on the night of the 18th. I could however, look out for the diurnal puffins from early in the day of the 19th.

The 18th of June 1936 was a hot and perfectly windless day with a tendency to thunder and mist. Such a heavy calm and bad visibility would, I felt, be a further check on the early return of the homing birds. This, and a day of work in the open, almost decided me not to go out that night to look at the marked nests in the knoll, and in the crevices of the wall where the petrels nested. I had already, as a precaution, glanced at all the nests during the day, and found no returned birds. The three shearwater nests had each contained a cold egg.

Nevertheless, as it was really an easy thing to do, I ran out to the knoll just before going to bed at 11.45 that evening. So near midsummer it was not a very dark night. There was no moon, but the stars were dancing between light clouds. The shearwaters had not yet started their screaming. I could hear only the crooning of the storm-petrels in the walls of the meadow. It was warm and very still.

There was nothing in burrows F and G. Neither RS 2255 nor RV 7569 had returned. Their eggs were still cold.

I yawned. Perhaps I was a bit early. I ought to go back and doze in the arm-chair for an hour or so, and then inspect the burrows. It was only a formality after all, a precaution against the seemingly impossible happening.

But when I lifted the sod to nest C, Caroline was there incubating her egg—it was warm—as if she had never travelled by boat, train and car to Start Point!

I took Caroline up carefully, to make quite sure, by a repeated examination of her leg-ring by the light of my torch, that it was not her mate, young Carol III, that I had in my hands. Then I stroked her, as I had so often done before. There was no other way in which I could let her know my new regard for her. But she appeared to be entirely unmoved in this show of affection. Only she did not attempt to snap at me, as so many younger birds would have. Familiarity had bred a large measure of indifference to these curious irregular visits of five-fingered hands groping through the ceiling of her home to take her up so gently yet firmly. This handling was a phenomenon, an inconvenience which must be put up with, since no real harm came of it.

I thought then that Lack must have released the birds in Devon very early that day, or even that he had decided, for some unforseen reason, to let them go when he reached the mainland of Pembrokeshire yesterday. But when his letter came two days later it told me that the surviving shearwater—Caroline—had been released at Start Point at 2 p.m. on 18th June. And I had picked her up exactly 9¾ hours later.

If Caroline returned over the sea-route of 225 miles, she had therefore made a bee-line flight of 23 miles an hour. But a shearwater does not fly like a bee; its air speed, due to its swinging deviating flight, must always be greater than its surface speed (i.e. its actual rate of progress). We might safely say that it had to travel at 30 miles an hour in order to cover 225 miles in 9¾ hours. This in itself is good travelling, and does not allow for resting or feeding by the way. Her success, I thought, was tremendous. I pictured how helpless I would have been under similar circumstances: transported by boat, train, and car, and then, supposing I had wings but no navigational instruments, thrown over a cliff into the English Channel. Could I have found Skokholm in 9¾ hours? Could I have found Skokholm at all?

Well then, how did Caroline find her way so easily and quickly?

If Caroline travelled overland—and the fact that she flew seawards straight out of sight when released at Start Point suggests that she did not—she had more time to spare. She would have had to get along at a ground speed of 13 to 14 miles an hour in order to cross 80 miles of Devon and 60 miles of the Bristol Channel in 9¾ hours.

It is clear, at least, that Caroline knew the way. She had no time for searching. She recognized in what direction Skokholm lay and made for it. She was in a tearing hurry to get home to the egg, which, in her absence, had not been incubated by Carol III. Carol III, indeed, was blissfully unaware of these things—he may well have been away on holiday (Biscay?) over the period of his mate's enforced defection of two days and a night.

* * * * *

Of the six puffins two were recaught at their burrows five days later. Of the three petrels one was recovered in its crevice six days later. Probably all returned earlier than this, but I found that these two species were awkward to handle. The puffins were now feeding young and it was difficult to catch them at all during the spasmodic visits they made to the burrows; while storm-petrels easily deserted their crevices if handled night after night. In future I would not use these species in homing trials.

For our success with Caroline was provocative. It suggested further experiment. We had merely learned a little about the homing power of the shearwater: that it could return very quickly when transported and released 140 miles distant and with a formidable land mass between it and its home. But how it did so, what the mechanism of this homing might be, we had not learned.

It was possible to surmise that Caroline was familiar with the topography of the English Channel and knew exactly where Skokholm lay in relation to Start Point. Or else that she had a very special homing sense, Riviere's 'sense of geographical position,' by which, no matter where released, she could orientate herself and fly straight home.

To prove the second hypothesis it was necessary to get shearwaters to return from places outside their normal geographical range.

The opportunity to do this came a few days later, when I made a visit to the Faroe Islands, that remote and little-visited group which lies half-way between the Shetlands and Iceland.

But I would not take Caroline with me. Caroline had already won her laurels for the season. And the loss of two shearwaters *en route* for Start Point was a warning of what might happen, in spite of great care, to valuable birds. It was this loss that suggested to me that the best subjects for this long-range test from the Faroes would be the mates of these dead birds. It seemed hardly likely that they would hatch their egg and rear their chick alone. In fact, I found that in the eight days following the loss of their mates these two birds were at their nests only irregularly.

The widow of RS 2255 happened to be on the egg when, at the moment of leaving the island on 15th June, I visited the knoll to collect the birds. But the widower of RV 7569 was away at sea; his egg was cold. I must find another bird.

I opened the nearest nest and found the lady AG 702 incubating. Ringed in 1930, she was, next to Caroline, the oldest surviving inhabitant of the village. Curiously enough she too had been once a mate of the lost RS 2255, in 1931 and 1932. In 1933 RS 2255 had picked up with his present mate, the youngster RS 2283 (now a widow and three breeding seasons old); while old AG 702 had also mated with a young bird in 1933, RS 2296, with whom she still cohabited. It seemed appropriate as well as perhaps whimsical to take these two wives of the lost RS 2255 with me to the Faroes. Also they were in my hand now, and I was in a hurry.

I packed AG 702 and RS 2283, each in one of a two-compartment wooden box which I had bedded with hay under fresh sheep's sorrel and grass blades.

It was a typical midsummer day when I said *au revoir* to the village on the knoll. Swifts and swallows were flying north over the island on a belated migration, swinging into the faint northerly breeze. The sea was as pale as the noon sky, and the air over the heathery fields was dancing with the radiation of the sun's heat.

On the long train journey I had to be careful to keep the box with the shearwaters in the shade. I watched over the innocent travellers with the deepest anxiety.

CHAPTER XIV

IN THE FAROE ISLANDS

IN spite of the heat the birds survived the train journey to
Edinburgh, and on the evening of the second day it was
cool enough as the Danish steamer *Primula* moved out of
the Firth of Forth. It was much too stuffy to keep the
shearwaters in my cabin, as I first attempted. I had opened
the port-hole three times, and the steward had shut it three
times; and at last he explained why—the ship was so small
that she rolled her sides under in the least wind. The
man sharing my cabin had told me he did not mind even
if—as I had warned him—the birds were to make a noise
at night; he always slept through the roaring of traffic at
home. He was a good-humoured Yorkshireman who was
going to Iceland to teach the Icelanders how to smoke and
cure herrings. And he lived up to his statement that noise
could not disturb his sleep. He snored as powerfully as
any excited shearwater.

I took the crate containing the two birds to the bridge
and made a clean breast of the affair. Captain Ekholdt was
delighted. At dinner that night—without warning to me
—he announced to the other passengers 'the interesting
experiment.' He said I must promise to let them all know
if the birds returned to Skokholm. I could have as many
sardines as I liked from the galley. He would personally
take care of the birds until I was ready to release them.
That night, pooh-poohing my advice, he stowed the box
in the shelter of the chart house, close to his bed.

By the next morning however, the box was banished to
the shade of the awnings on the boat deck. The shearwaters had spoken to each other in the darkness with
unnecessary emphasis, Ekholdt explained. The noise had
been surprising, interesting, boring, and at last positively

annoying. To get any sleep at all he had had to shift the birds out of hearing.

I was glad, for it was cooler out there. I was still anxiously watching the health of the two villagers from the knoll. I had not been pleased with the idea of their facing the fumes of officers' pipes and cigarettes. Shearwaters can exist in stuffy holes under the earth, but tobacco was an untried element.

Ekholdt was worried about their feeding. I think he considered me a little callous in not giving them the fish he proffered from both tin and refrigerator. But I knew that a fast of a few days is as nothing to the shearwater. I felt that the less they were disturbed the better.

'And water, you must surely give the birds some water?' he protested.

To humour him I did so, but I had to send away the fresh water he ordered. I asked for a bucket of salt water. Trying not to look surprised (for the fact that a sea-bird naturally drinks salt water had evidently only just struck him), he assented. I ducked each bird under once. And then with difficulty, as Ekholdt still pleaded, I stuffed first a slice of cold-stored plaice and then a sardine down the throat of each shearwater. They protested, biting my fingers.

'I am doing it, not to please the birds or myself, but to please you,' I said to Ekholdt.

In the struggle a fine mess of fish had spread over my hands and clothes and over the plumage of the birds. I dipped the shearwaters completely under the water again. They were clean once more. I replaced them in their boxes.

The *Primula* left the North Sea and glided through Stronsay Firth, the passage which cuts the Orkneys in two. She bucked into the Atlantic swell as she headed north-north-west for the Faroes. The little black guillemots, shags, cormorants, gulls, and terns gradually vanished astern, and at last only the fulmar petrels were left. They glided endlessly, effortlessly, around the ship.

At 8 p.m. Ekholdt gave me the position of the ship as 60° 15′ N., 4° 20′ W., that is about one hundred miles from the Faroes. I held up RS 2283 over the port rail of the bridge and gave her a little push with my hands.

She swept away grandly, made two or three tacks, and continued to fly away from the ship. The visibility was poor, but I held her in view with the glasses for about half a mile. She kept onwards, flying almost due south into the light wind.

Back in the chart-room we pricked off her direction on a map. By coincidence or by design she was, on that bearing, making direct for Skokholm, six hundred miles distant, on an almost straight course through the Inner Hebrides, the North Channel, and the Irish Sea.

'Wonderful,' said Ekholdt. 'That, I think, is what you call instinct?'

He looked at me for confirmation. Rather than appear continually a blockhead, I nodded vaguely. I felt, however, that this initial start was too good to be more than coincidence. Like Caroline leaving Start Point, perhaps RS 2283 had simply flown directly away from the ship because it had unpleasant associations for her. I had purposely released her on the side of the ship facing the south-west, the side nearest home.

At six next morning we were entering the grey islands of the Faroes, whose mountainous tops were quite hidden in grey rolling mists. Grey and grey and grey. My poor AG 702 was to start under dismal and difficult auspices.

The *Primula* was headed due north along the eastern face of the main island of Streymoy, so it did not matter which side I released AG 702.

There was a cool wind from the north-east. I threw her over the port side. She gathered her wings and circled around the bow of the ship, into the wind. In a few seconds she vanished into the mist.

*   *   *   *   *

With the exception of the Westmann Islands, which lie south of Iceland and in a latitude only a little higher than that of the Faroes, the Faroes are the most northerly breeding grounds of the Manx, or indeed any other, shearwater in the world. The Manx, however, is the only shearwater breeding in these two groups. I wondered if these two Skokholm-breeding Manx shearwaters would, as a result of this transportation, be drawn to join their brothers, the Faroe-breeding shearwaters? Certainly perhaps AG 702 might, being released right inside Farish territorial waters. But perhaps RS 2283 had been released too far south to be affected by Farish shearwaters?

This homing experiment was designed with the object of answering such questions.

I was especially anxious to find some colonies of Manx shearwaters in the Faroes. I looked forward with excitement to meeting a familiar bird in these strange and wild islands. Probably the Farish Manx shearwater would be identical with ours in appearance and habits—and yet, by living so far north, it was certainly, to me, a strange bird. To me it would be a race with subtly different if indefinable national traits, as different as the Welsh people are from the Cornish. And would it, did it, mingle with our shearwaters, 700 miles farther south? Did the Faroe Manx shearwater fly even to the Bay of Biscay, 1,300 miles away? Certainly not to feed by day in the summer; that would surely be too far? But perhaps on migration in winter it reached Biscay?

These were vain questions, only to be answered by extensive ringing, for which I was not then prepared. I had, in fact, only a few rings in my pocket—British rings are not supposed to be used outside the British Isles. Nor had I come solely to look at shearwaters. An irresistible curiosity about remote islands, their people, and their birds, had drawn me to visit the Faroes; and in particular I was looking for two things: a completely unsophisticated island people, and a rare bird called Leach's fork-tailed petrel.

In Tórshavn I found a glimmering of both. Ice cream and lipstick, radio and cinema, are available in the multi-coloured, corrugated-iron capital of the Faroes. But there you will also see stocky little men on stocky little ponies, riding in from lonely *bygd* and *gard*, from hamlet and farm hidden in the all but inaccessible glens and ravines of the main island of Streymoy. These men wear the sprightly, almost gnome-like, national woollen dress of close-fitting knee-breeches, decorated waistcoat, bebuttoned jacket, and jaunty, striped, tasselled, night-cappish hat. There is a rich innocent look in their weather-wrinkled eyes—they are thinking of their sod-roofed homes, their sheep and cattle, their potatoes and the fishing, in returning to which they must first cross the high backbone of the island, the stony *fjeldmerken*, a thousand feet up in the grey mists where the whimbrel and purple sandpiper dwell. Others must go by boat to their homes on the smaller islands of the group.

At the 'National' library—the Faroes are a Danish dependency, but if they were only strong enough financially the 30,000 inhabitants would be what they prefer to be, an independent nation—I learned that the bird life of the islands was 'very splendid, no one has examine her scientifically, but I assure you there are not hundreds but only *millions* of rare birds in the backward islands. Do not ask me the names of the birds anyhow, I will not be informed intelligently for a scientist like yourself.'

I confess that this proud title, more than once bestowed on me in my travels, was as undeserved as it was flattering. Without troubling to deny it—so vain is man—I tried to live up to it as, together, the librarian and I searched for the 'backward islands' on a map. I was excited, if a little suspicious, by the airy reference to millions of rare birds. . . .

In the end we decided I should most likely find two of these millions, namely, Leach's fork-tailed petrel and the Manx shearwater, on Hestur, or if not, then on Koltur, both small islands on the Atlantic side of the Faroes.

I never found the fork-tailed petrel. But I stumbled on two colonies of the Manx shearwater. The first was in a tremendous *fuglabjerg*, or bird-fowling cliff, on the west side of Hestur. To reach the spot we had to walk through dense mist by a slippery grass path on the edge of the precipice.

Hestur, although 1,382 feet high, is scarcely four miles long. It seemed to me, as we scrambled along the path in the mist, that we must have already gone twice round the island, so interminable was the journey. The green mountain was a thrusting shield—so steep was it—against which my left hand now pushed, now grabbed, to steady myself. On my right was the precipice. I knew this because the grass on the right of the path dropped almost sheer away into the mist. I did not need to be warned to keep my feet in the narrow sheep track, as Towror and his fellow cragsmen, Rolant, Joen, Jacob, and Thorlief, had warned me. I knew only too well that one step out of that three-inch groove on to that wet green apron, and nothing could have saved a man. I am used to heights and rough climbing, but I was uneasy during that seemingly long march. I acknowledged a tightness of the breast.

If we could have seen the sea it would have been more reassuring. But we were a thousand feet up, there was neither sight nor sound of the sea, but only the mist hanging over the unseen chasm. We could not even see the leading man a few yards ahead—only the net of his fowling rod bobbed backwards over us. The ghostly forms of the three boys, Hjilgrim, Gudmund, and Hans, skipping recklessly along behind me, were disturbing. I muttered words of caution, but they only laughed, not understanding anything except that my careful steps signified to them that I was timid, and that they by contrast were bold and brave. Or they may have been excited solely by the expectation of fowling. Certainly it was a holiday for them, a fine summer day which must be savoured to the full with dancing eyes, tongues, and limbs. The mist I cursed was

part of their lives—I might as well have cursed the sunshine at the equator, for mist at Hestur is just as unrelenting.
The mists never left Hestur while I stayed on the island.

At last we came to a break in the cliff. Here was a more
level platform on which we could sit and stretch our legs.
A hoary stake driven into the ground served as a hitching-
post for a rusted wire which disappeared into the mist
below. Now and then a fulmar petrel lurched into the
brief radius of our vision. We could hear its breeding-cackle
faintly, from ledges out of sight.

We were huddled together, smiling at each other, I with
relief at finishing, for the time being, with that cliff path.
Beads of mist dripped from eyebrows and noses, and ran
down cheeks, to settle coldly inside heated necks. My
corduroys were thoroughly wet, but the stout Farish woollen
jerseys worn by the others were successfully resisting the
moisture by means of their outer surface of stiff springy
hair-like wool or kemp.

Towror seized the wire and gave a violent tug. The
post quivered—no more. He grunted, satisfied, and began
walking swiftly backwards into space. Using the wire,
hand over hand, he vanished backwards and downwards.
His disappearance was splendidly theatrical.

I leaned over to look at him. It was much clearer down
there, and I could just glimpse the sea. Towror was
spinning slowly in mid air, fifty feet down, well above a
grassy ledge. As he turned on the wire, like a joint on a
spit, he continued to drop rapidly. I remembered I had
seen something like it before—oh, yes, a spider, or rather, a
caterpillar jerking down a silken thread.

'You!' Jacob patted my back, and as I rolled over to
face him, he began tying a rope around my middle. 'You
hold wire, we hold rope. Towror watches there.'

His thumb jerked downwards. His face was one wide
encouraging smile.

There are times when I wish I were stubby and wiry—
for that is the breed which does best at this sort of job.

Instead I myself become ten times and my feet twenty times as heavy once I leave the ground. I am all lop-sided, top-heavy, completely lacking in equipoise. I went down, or rather I was lowered down, to Towror like a sack of pig-iron. There were tears in my eyes and bruises on my knuckles and my hands were red-hot (literally, for the palms were bleeding) when I landed on the ledge ninety feet below. But I managed to smile at the grinning Towror, a smile as sick as the inside of my stomach.

Towror was pointing to Jacob.

High above us, on the bulge of the cliff, Jacob was holding the wire with his hands only, and looking fixedly at me. He was anxious to show me how it was done. I collapsed in a large puffin hole, and, thus comfortably wedged, waved my hand for the performance to begin. I knew that I had not come down very fast, in spite of my torn hands. Jacob, however, would hardly beat Towror for a speedy descent.

Jacob did not try. He did something far more beautiful and spectacular. He worked his way to the left for a few yards, and then, holding the wire, he bent his legs for a spring. Up and into the air he sailed, swinging in a wide arc and landing far to the right on the sheer wall of a buttress. He broke the force of his contact there with feet and knees flexing, like a long jumper on level ground. But he did not stop. He used the buffer-like action of his feet and knees to give a stronger impetus to make a wider arc to the left. He bounced back to a position farther left than his starting-point. Then he was off again in a splendid jump farther than ever to the right.

It was magnificent, this pendulum monkey-jumping on a rugged cliff a thousand feet sheer above the sea. Magnificent, but, I thought, not without great danger. In time, the wire must grind thin at the fulcrum, against the cliff, where the strain was greatest. Poise and confidence were needed for such a performance—I shuddered to think what would happen if Jacob lost his poise, or if the wire

M

twisted while he was flying through the air; he would be smashed sideways, or thrown on his back against the cliff.

Jacob did not lose his poise, nor did the wire break. For one second Jacob clung to his last landing-place, far to the left, and looking down, his wide face grinned towards mine. But his glance also swept the lower cliff. I realized a moment later that he was looking for a landing-ground lower down. He swung to the right again, but as he flew through the air, he lowered himself swiftly on the wire, thus striking the rock to the right much below his first level. But his feet met the rock expertly, and he shot off again. Two more such daring downward leaps and he was clear of the buttress. Hand over hand, he now dropped swiftly down, until, still swaying, he seized the right moment of the pendulum to alight beside us.

While the others came down, more soberly, I had time to look about me. We were on a rough grassy platform about six yards square. No sheep had ever grazed here—the ledge was as gay with flowers as are the sod-roofed homes of the Hestur folk. I saw sea-pinks, a large buttercup, ragged robin, white scurvy-grass, angelica, and a splendid blue crane's-bill which Towror called *Bléblomstur*.

Joen thrust his feet into some bird burrows at the edge of the cliff, and began sweeping at a few puffins which were flying past with fish in their bills. But it was a bad moment—the puffins were not yet making a real flight. They were few and they flew high and wide. After a desperate attempt to reach out over the cliff at these, young Joen received a sharp warning from the older Towror. So he contented himself with sweeping up a fulmar petrel.

The Farish fowling net is about four feet long and two wide, and has a handle fifteen feet long—quite a heavy instrument to fling into the wind when one is precariously balanced on a crumbling earth ledge a thousand feet sheer above the white line of the surf. I tried it, cautiously, myself. The net must lie on the windward side of you, flat on the cliff, the end of the handle kept on the ground so that when you swing it out, with your two hands grasping the handle higher up, the end can be levered against the earth to give additional force and speed to your effort. Birds reach the cliffs flying head to wind, and this is a help, as you can naturally hurl the net more easily down wind upon them.

At my very first sweep I found a fulmar in the net.

Found is the right word. True, I had seen the fulmar coming, but more to try the weight of the instrument than anything else I had made a pass at it. The bird had slipped into the net. It was really an accident, I thought. But the others applauded loudly. Luckily I managed to conceal my own amazement by keeping my face and my fixed smile towards the sea.

The net I threw up towards the assembled group. A captured fulmar ejects the foulest-smelling oil, steadily, for about a minute. I preferred that the others dealt with it.

Joen broke its neck as it lay in the net. Then, pulling it out, he tossed it towards Towror. Towror threw it laughingly at Hjilgrim. Hjilgrim took careful aim at Thorlief. It was a great joke, this despised fulmar, this stinking bird. . . . Thorlief hurled it smartly and with success at the back of Hans's neck. Yes, you ate adult fulmar in the Faroes, but only if forced to by lack of other food. It tasted like paper, or worse. Hans, insulted, made a feint to throw it back at Thorlief. It was a well-sold baby—Thorlief ducked, but as he rose again, the fulmar, slammed along by Hans, caught him full in the face. There was another roar of laughter. This miserable bird! This bird which, with its green-brown oil, drove the useful guillemots and razorbills and puffins from the cliffs more and more each year! Thorlief threw the bird far out over my head, thus acknowledging that young Hans had got the best of it, and, thus, good-naturedly, preventing the development of any warmer horse-play in our present situation.

Thorlief was wise. Heads should be kept cool on the cliff. The dead fulmar spun downwards to the sea.

I proceeded to spoil the excellent impression I had made by further attempts to catch puffin and fulmar. Growing bolder, I reached out farther, so far that Towror fixed a rope about my waist and held to it. But I failed to net another bird.

Meanwhile the boys had pulled out from the holes which honeycombed the ledge several adult and young puffins. The adults were necked, the young ones returned to their holes. This seemed to me hard lines on the chick and on the mate (which may or may not have been necked also), but the Farish people have a plausible excuse for this behaviour. They believe, or at least they tell you, that there are seven adult puffins to each burrow, that is, to each egg or chick, so that always one or two adults survive to look after egg or chick!

Hans and Gudmund also discovered a Manx shearwater sitting on an egg, and another on a newly hatched chick. I was glad, but could not from their excited talk discover why they did not attempt to kill the adult. But I supposed that the excuse used for killing adult puffins had not been recognized to hold good for the adult shearwater.

I picked the shearwater up. Yes, it was exactly like a Skokholm shearwater — plumage and size identical. I might have had Caroline in my hand, except that this Faroe bird was shyer—naturally, for it had not been handled often or ever before.

Because the peoples of the remoter islands of the Faroes live much on sea-birds, all these have been driven to the cliffs, the mountain tops, and other difficult places. They do not breed in accessible situations as they do at Skokholm. Manx shearwaters in the Faroes nest only in such burrows as these on high cliffs where there are small platforms on which they can obtain alighting and digging room. Here they have few enemies, far fewer than at Skokholm. The men of the Faroes take them, chiefly the fledgelings during August, when these are at a fat stage. They are then reckoned the tastiest of all sea-bird dishes. But there are

The farm on Koltur where Carl Niclasen lives.   The homing shearwater was taken from the cliffs on the other side of the mountain in the background

few other predators.   Great black-backed gulls are scarce, there are few ravens, and no buzzards.   Moreover for these shearwaters there is no laborious travelling overland with consequent exposure to attack.   The shearwater can alight easily beside the burrow and can get away with the same ease, even in a dead calm, simply by tumbling over the edge and spreading its wings in space.   So, too, the young bird, when its turn comes, has a splendid advantage over the Skokholm nestling; the Faroe fledgeling cannot fail to reach the sea from its cliff burrow.

While the adult was in my hand the idea came into my head that I should take it home with me and release it at Skokholm, and thus complete the homing experiment by a test both ways.   I began explaining the idea to Jacob, who spoke English fairly well, but I could not make him understand properly; and, realizing that I could not easily keep the shearwater with me during the rest of my stay on Hestur and until I sailed for home, I gave up the plan. Perhaps later, I could go and collect one of these adult shearwaters?

*   *   *   *   *

Actually it was on a similar ledge on the smaller neighbouring island of Koltur that I collected a shearwater for the homing test, in a situation that entailed a much less hazardous walk and climb to reach it.   Here Carl Niclasen, farmer, fisherman, fowler, and shipwright, agreed, with obvious pleasure, to pay visits and await the return of this bird, which I was to ring so that he could recognize it.

We took the shearwater from a burrow containing a chick about a week old.   Now, as we have seen earlier in this book, the adult does not remain by day with the chick after it is a week old, except on rare occasions.   This chick would be about a fortnight old when I released its parent in six or seven days' time.   I had to explain to Carl that the parents would only return at night, and then ask him if he was prepared to visit the place at night.   It seemed rather an impossible proposition, and I was in two minds about proceeding further with the experiment. To add to my difficulty Carl nodded his head and smiled at everything I said, which, as he only understood English very imperfectly, was, I thought, remarkable. I remember that this was a trick I sometimes used when bombarded in another tongue with questions which I did not understand or wanted to get past quickly.

When I left the Faroes the adult was very lively in the box which Carl had made for it. I walked into Tórshavn with the box under my arm, in plenty of time to meet the homeward-bound *Primula* which was due to return to the Faroes from Iceland.

The Prime Minister and Minister of War for Denmark had arrived in the capital on an official visit in the lighthouse tender *Argus*. 'Koltur,' as I called the shearwater, popped up her head through the bars of her prison-box to look at these celebrities. She and I watched the Tórshavn people performing a Farish chain-dance in the street, men and women in national costume prancing in a great circle to the music of their own voices raised in an old, old ballad said to be of two hundred verses.

'Koltur' caused some excitement when the Prime Minister, a little weary perhaps of the endless country dance, spotted her sticking-up head and came over to me and stroked her, and said a few words which I did not understand. This effrontery Koltur repaid with a swift pass at the minister's beautiful white beard. I merely said 'Skrapur!' which is Farish for shearwater. I was rather ashamed of the bird's behaviour, and, as well, a little nervous that I was in unlawful possession of an adult shearwater. I was not sure of the bird-fowling laws of the Farish state, but I knew they were important and rigid. There were two policemen (the only ones in Faroe) and the governor of the islands standing close behind the Danish ministers.

However, we saluted each other with a raising of hands, and I moved on to the dock where the *Primula* was now entering. They probably took me for a curio-hunting tourist. And tourists are privileged, and must be humoured. A tourist bureau was just being set up in the town.

Captain Ekholdt was amused to find me bringing another shearwater on board. He ordered it to solitary confinement on the boat deck.

*   *   *   *   *

At 3 p.m. on 8th July I placed on Koltur's leg a ring numbered RW 7664, and released her close to Leith harbour. As she had been six days in the box I had decided not to risk a 17-hour train journey with her across Scotland, England, and Wales. She skimmed vigorously away down the Firth of Forth, heading eastwards for the North Sea.

I reached Skokholm on the 10th, and the same night went out to the village on the knoll and picked up both AG 702 and RS 2283, released twelve and eleven days before, on the journey north.

As for the shearwater from Koltur, she had almost gone out of my mind in a week or so. Then Carl Niclasen wrote to me by the Koltur post-boat on 13th August to say that 'the skrapur returned to Koltur on the 9th August, with ring on its leg numbered RW 7664. I found the skrapur in the company of its young on that day. With good wishes from all at Koltur. N. C. Niclasen.'

Carl had understood far more than I had supposed. I had underrated his enthusiasm and tenacity. Nothing is too much trouble with the fine peoples of the little islands, whose lives are regulated less by the monetary considera- tion than by the spirit of comradeship and mutual help and love. To visit that wild crag every day for over a month was a labour of love. To visit it at night must have been even more testing. But as a fact I never discovered whether Carl found RW 7664 by day or by night. That he recovered the bird at all, and quoted the ring number to prove it, was astonishing enough.

CHAPTER XV

MID-JULY in the knoll village. The honey-coloured bells of the wood-sage were again hanging out, with creeping St John's wort twined in the wiry stems below. Opposite, on the garden wall, foxglove and yarrow and viscid ragwort held up their torches to the gentle summer wind. Above, the skylark was still singing.

In the sun-dried streets of the village a little wild thyme had come into flower and some minute plants of the lesser skullcap shot up through the rabbit-grazed grass and sheep's sorrel and scarlet pimpernel. In the burrows the downy young shearwaters had hatched and were growing sturdy. I looked through the nests to see what adult birds might be sent off on further homing tests. It was getting late in the season, but we were anxious to continue the work, which had been so successful.

Could I risk any more old-timers? My supply of these was dwindling. Caroline, 1929 bird, I would not risk again, nor AG 702, 1930 bird, rashly taken to the Faroes but successfully returned. But why risk any of the knoll inmates? Why not go outside and get shearwaters from burrows elsewhere in the home meadow?

My excuse was pure laziness. To find suitable shallow burrows, easy of examination like those of the knoll, was quite a formidable business. But at last I tried it, digging for a whole day, following tortuous burrows, and in the end, when pieces of the meadow looked like entrenchments of a modern battlefield in miniature, I found I had saved only four accessible burrows containing chicks. By saved I mean that I had found and fitted with an observation sod only four burrows suitable for daily recording. Other burrows fell in, some were too confused and labyrinthine altogether, and several were without egg or chick.

David Lack was in London arranging transport for long-distance releases at this time. Meanwhile Frank Elder, returning from a visit to Skokholm, took with him RW 9915, brooding a chick in one of these four burrows, and also RW 8080, a bird brooding a chick in the knoll. Elder took them out to the Isle of May in the Firth of Forth. RW 9915 he released on the west side of the May; it flew south-west and then turned south-east for the Bass Rock on a course that, if continued would bring it south around England on an 870-mile sea trip to Skokholm. North around Scotland the sea journey is 800 miles. RW 9915 was recovered at Skokholm twelve days later.

RW 8080, released on the east side of the May, flew due east, and vanished low over the waves. I recovered it twenty-eight days later; it was feeding its chick. Both these birds may have got back earlier, but at this time of year they would only be visiting the island irregularly at night for the purpose of feeding young.

Later, in 1938, RW 8080 returned in twenty-nine days when released at Le Havre, France. She is still a valued inhabitant of the village as I write.

I now took RW 9915, freshly home from the Isle of May, and another from the four meadow burrows, and sent them across the Atlantic by arrangement with Lack. The report came later that both survived the journey to America, but were in a weak condition when released near Boston, Massachusetts. We did not expect them to return that year. But I am afraid I never recovered them in the succeeding years.

Eight adults were also sent off on the S.S. *Grantully Castle* for release on her route to South Africa. For this experiment I was reduced to seizing six adults which I found sitting at night outside a group of deep burrows west of the knoll. The other two were from the knoll itself. I selected that rather tiresome lady Baby, wife (1933), divorcee (1934), and widow (1935) of Adam, as I happened to find her sitting in an empty burrow on the night I made the collection; and RS 2292, a 1933-ringed adult which had lost her egg earlier in the year and therefore could face the long voyage over the equator with no home ties to trouble her.

As these releases in the South Atlantic would not take place until the end of July I did not expect the voyagers to return until 1937. We were disappointed to receive a report that none of them even crossed the equator. For some reason or other they travelled badly. The technique of caring for them on board had not been applied successfully. Whereas Koltur had spent nearly a week travelling from the Faroes, without showing signs of weakness, Baby and RS 2292 died while they were crossing the Bay of Biscay, one day out of port. Five of the others had to be released in weak condition between Spain and North Africa. The last died before it could be released in the same area.

Only one of the five survivors ever returned to Skokholm. RW 9918 was picked up in the burrows west of the knoll on 5th June 1937. This bird had been released off Corunna, north-west Spain, about 250 miles beyond the known range—according to our ringing results—of Skokholm shearwaters.

In addition to these long-distance tests in 1936, we tried two releases inland. Kenrick, who had correlated the meteorological data with Coward's collection of shearwaters recovered inland (see Chapter XII, page 140), came to Skokholm, and took back with him RW 8057, a bird picked up from an empty burrow outside the knoll. Inland releases would of course provide useful light on this theory of an inland migration propounded by Coward. Kenrick released RW 8057 from the terrace of his house near Birmingham at 8.50 p.m. on 14th July. It flew off south-west, that is, in a direct line for Skokholm. But if it ever returned to the island I did not discover it.

A shearwater from the selfsame burrow, released at Evesham at the same time, came back in the following spring. These two, taken from an empty burrow, were not ideal subjects, for they had no family cares to induce them to return. However, we repeated the experiment in 1937 with two birds from empty burrows sent at the same time (13th–14th July) as in 1936; the Evesham bird this time returned in five days, and the Birmingham bird in nineteen days. Thus, although it was after midsummer and the birds apparently had no family cares, there was yet some stimulus that caused them to return to the island.

There were other successful inland releases in 1937. A shearwater taken from an egg in a burrow outside the knoll was dropped from Northenden Bridge into the Mersey on 23rd May. It flew west down river, and was recovered at the nest on 6th June. Another was taken to Limerick. An obliging Irish guard stopped the train on the Shannon Bridge while Stephen Marchant threw the bird into the wide river. It flew west for the sea. It was recovered at Skokholm a week later.

The best times for an inland release were made by two birds from the knoll: RS 2317, a staunch lady registered in 1933 and now with her second husband; and EXP 106, a young lady just registered (4th April 1937) who was the third wife of a 1933 male. These two females were taken to Frensham Ponds, Surrey, and released at dusk on 8th June. They flew over the water, making a wide circuit before going away in a direction between south and west. This, if held to strictly, would have brought them to the English Channel; but there was no evidence, of course, that they held to this line of flight. Skokholm lies some 220 miles slightly north of west from Frensham. If the birds flew straight to the nearest coast and thence by sea the mileage is nearly doubled.

Both were the first of the shearwaters to return to the island on the following night. Their eggs had been cold and deserted during the day. I went out towards midnight.

The south horizon was heavy and black, but there was still a light in the northern sky. So far no shearwaters had started to scream. It was a bit early; but soon, I thought, perhaps the males would be home and taking up incubation in the absence of their mates.

Instead I found both Frensham ladies on well-warmed eggs. It was a quarter of an hour to midnight. They must have arrived about 11.30 in the late dusk, slipping in silently. They must have travelled at least 220 miles in 24 hours, or by sea at twice that speed. Allowing for some deviation of flight and a few moments (of the twenty-four hours) for drinking and bathing, the speed of the return by sea must have been 30 miles an hour, which is near the true (ground) speed of the shearwater. By whatever route they flew they must have orientated and 'got off the mark' very swiftly indeed, which is the more remarkable when we consider that Frensham Ponds are more than fifty miles inland and presumably in an area entirely unfamiliar to the shearwater.

This success was the prelude to a far more difficult homing experiment. We intended to send these two birds not only out of the known range of Skokholm shearwaters, but also right out of the geographical range of the Manx shearwater as a species. The known geographical range covers the North Atlantic and as far south as Brazil. But as far as is known the Manx shearwater does not enter the Mediterranean, or its ramification, the Adriatic.

I allowed the two Frensham homers a month's rest before sending them to Venice, on the innermost shore of the Adriatic Sea. They left the island on the afternoon of 7th July. I sent them to London by train, whence they reached Venice by air on the 9th. This was quick work, and the birds arrived in first-class condition in consequence.

Writing to me under the date of 10th July 1937, Alan Napier, British Consul at Venice, gave the following details of the release:

The wing that flew from Venice to Skokholm

Salmon

Flashlight photograph of adult Manx shearwater

The case containing the shearwaters arrived at 16 o'clock local time yesterday, and the birds were released at 19.50 (18.50 G.M.T.). Place of release: lagoon ¼ mile south of Venice. Particulars of weather: clear sky, sun setting behind a bank of clouds on horizon. Temperature of air at time of release, 73° F. Water dead calm, suspicion of breeze from E. The birds, which were first dipped in the water, and then thrown simultaneously into the air, flew off in a southerly direction, but one of them had wheeled off towards the west when last seen. The day had been fortunately cool after heavy storms during the night of 8th–9th.

This experiment was so late in the year, with the eggs in the burrows about hatching, that I felt it was unlikely that the Venice birds would return in 1937. I kept a strict watch on the burrows, however, as I was interested as well to study the behaviour of the two males. The old male RS 2313, mate of EXP 106, incubated the egg for six out of the first ten days. The moon, however, was now waxing, and this, added to the absence of his mate, caused him to desert by day. At least I did not trace him after the 19th. And his wife did not return from Venice that year.

The young male, husband of the old female RS 2317, stuck to the egg for seven days. Perhaps he, too, might have deserted if, fortunately, the chick had not hatched on the seventh day. This event, setting loose the fresh impulses of nursing and feeding, may have heartened the young male to continue in his wife's absence. Not only did he, single-handed, dry out and brood the chick for the first two days, but he slipped away on the third night, left the chick for the day, and returned to feed it on the fourth, and, in spite of the moon, on subsequent nights. Fortunately the weather was warm, so that the downy chick, which is normally brooded for seven days, did not suffer from cold. This state of affairs continued up to the night of 23rd July.

On that night I was strolling about the island with three friends. We had early looked at the 'Venice' nests in the knoll, and found only the deserted egg and the solitary

chick. There was a strong westerly wind and a bright
moon, by the light of which we hoped to catch sight of
the swift forms of the storm-petrels dancing in the air
above their nesting crevices in the walls.

Just before we turned in at 1 a.m. (midnight G.M.T.),
we had a second peep at the knoll homes. It seemed rather
a waste of time, for we had not heard any shearwaters
calling over the island, though one or two had come in
silently, swinging past us with a brief hiss of wings.

Nest H was still empty, the egg cold. But even before
I opened nest A I could hear the chuckling of an adult
and the little satisfied squeaks of a chick being fed. Quite
a conversation was going on. Perhaps, I thought idly,
the chick and his father were discussing the outrageous
disappearance of the mother. I lifted the sod as a matter
of routine, to check up the number of the male's ring.

My torch showed both adults with the nestling. RS 2317
was home! Her new ring (her fifth, and in this year
numbered SAT 141) was proof positive.

We four men handled and stroked her in the moonlight
with something like awe. She was plump and glossy.
She had done herself well, in spite of the long voyage
from Venice.

When we had returned her I listened with my ear to the
turf over the nest. Her husband and chick received her
with characteristic little low greetings—and the (presumed)
discussion continued. I would have given much to have
been able to understand their conversation. As it is, truth
bids me suppose that it was unromantic enough: probably
the traveller, having flown home in anticipation of resuming
incubation, was a bit upset at finding a sturdy chick where
she expected an egg. But her mate having seemingly
accepted the situation, she probably swiftly adapted herself
to it. Whether her impulses to feed and brood the chick
were released and functioning that night of her return is
doubtful. Neither male nor female regurgitated on my
handling them—as adults commonly do at this stage—but

it is almost certain that the chick had already been fed by the male before our second inspection, for the young body seemed to be solid with food and fat.

How did RS 2317 find her way home from Venice? She had taken 14 days, 5 hours, and 10 minutes to (1) negotiate 3,700 miles by sea, or (2) cross Europe direct in 930 straight miles. In terms of plain arithmetic if she had negotiated (1) a sea-passage by the Straits of Messina and Gibraltar, she had travelled at a speed of nearly 11 miles an hour day and night, without food, rest, or deviation. However, it is safe to double the bee-line speed in order to arrive at the actual average surface speed of a shearwater. This gives us 22 miles an hour for the journey. If we allow six hours a day for resting and feeding, we must increase this speed by one-quarter, and so we get a speed of nearly 30 miles an hour. This is nearer the true flight speed of the Manx shearwater; but even so it presupposes that the bird had a comprehensive knowledge of the topography of the Mediterranean—and this we cannot grant to a bird that had never been there. It argues that RS 2317 was capable of flying south-east for 500 miles down the Adriatic, directly away from Skokholm, with the knowledge that once through the Strait of Otranto she could fly south-west for the Strait of Messina, and thence due west for Gibraltar. Then, and then only, once clear of Cape St Vincent in Portugal, could she head directly north for Skokholm.

Could she do all this? There is a small margin of time and speed to account for. We can allow her to waste one-quarter of her time in finding her way by sea; that would increase her speed to 40 miles an hour, about the average speed of a bird in good condition. There is just the possibility, then, that, given the above allowances, she did find her way by sea. But for myself I find it hard to believe that she resisted the mysterious 'pull' of home so far as to fly directly away from it in unknown waters, or that she could ever find her way so quickly by sea. I feel that the probability is she took some shorter cut, perhaps

over the Italian Apennines to the Gulf of Genoa (Mr Napier
noticed that one bird flew west, landwards, after release),
and then across France to the Bay of Biscay, which, as we
have seen, is the haunt of Skokholm shearwaters nearest
to the Mediterranean.   This course is more in line with
whatever influence Skokholm might exercise at that distance.

Of course, if this 'pull' exists and can act strongly, then
the bird should have flown directly across Europe to
Skokholm, that is to say, right across the High Alps and
France, 930 miles as the crow flies.   In that case, at a
surface speed of 10 miles an hour, she ought to have been
home in four days.   Did she reach home waters, perhaps,
in that time, and then rest and feed for 10 days?   This
seems too long a period of recuperation.

No; I incline to the belief that RS 2317, by some sense,
some physical mechanism unknown to man, aware that
Skokholm lay approximately just so (in our language,
north-west) from Venice, flew in that direction, but after
crossing Italy she was diverted by the sight of the Gulf
of Genoa.   After resting and feeding there, she continued
her westerly flight, which brought her into the Gulf of
Lyons.   Here she was embayed, and found herself obliged
to strike homewards over the south of France.   This
course would bring her to the Bay of Biscay.   Here, in
the sardine-filled waters, she could rest and feed among
other Skokholm shearwaters.   And here, perhaps, she
acquired that fat and glossy appearance which we noted
on finding her home at the nest with mate and chick.

*   *   *   *   *

What, meanwhile, had happened to EXP 106, the young
female released at Venice at the same time?   I feared very
much that she had fallen by the way.   We did not recover
her that summer.   When I sent a description of the shearwater homing experiments to *The Times* I was obliged to
post her there, in effect, as 'missing, believed lost.'

This article had a remarkable sequel.   It was published

on 24th September. On 25th November Lt.-Col. H. Delmé-Radcliffe wrote from Montreux, Switzerland, at the eastern end of the Lake of Geneva, that he had seen the missing shearwater from Venice on the lake.

Its left wing is obviously badly injured, and I do not think the bird is able to fly. It looks as if it had flown against a wire somewhere, but had managed to make its way by water somehow down to this lake, perhaps by way of the river Rhône? No bird of this species would ever come down here from the north, but one released from Venice would have to go north to reach its home.

His account was so conclusive that I felt it essential that the bird should be secured in order to prove its identity by the ring which, if it was my lost Venice bird, it would be wearing. I therefore cabled Lt.-Col. Delmé-Radcliffe, asking him to secure the bird by any means in his power.

Lt.-Col. Delmé-Radcliffe wrote, under date of 6th December, that he had been out in a boat after the bird, with Brigadier Norman. It was

a matter of great difficulty to secure the bird here. Shooting is strictly forbidden on the lake near Montreux, as it is one of the great pleasures of the public to watch the birds on the lake, and the birds are tame in consequence. Besides which I have no wish to take the life of this plucky little bird, who must have flown over the high Alps to get here, and he seems quite happy here, so we much prefer to watch him every day, as we do.

He added that the bird, though unable to fly, could swim and dive well, and did not allow a very near approach. Also:

another Englishman, who is not a naturalist, told Brigadier Norman, that he thought the bird was a female grebe. . . .

I wrote, after I had pondered on the advisability of going to Montreux myself, and asked Lt.-Col. Delmé-Radcliffe if some effort could be made to secure the bird alive, so that, if the wound could be healed, the shearwater might be

N

repatriated in home waters; as I agreed that it was not fair to take the bird's life in order to secure it.

Lt.-Col. Delmé-Radcliffe wrote that he himself was going away from Montreux, but that he would ask another keen observer to help me.

It is true that Major Crabbe is about 77 years of age (the English community here consists of very old people mostly, principally retired officers of the Army, Navy, and Civil Services, with their wives and relations. I myself am a retired army

Black-throated Diver   Guillemot

Manx Shearwater   Grebe

officer just on 72 years of age, but many others are older than I am), but he is interested in all natural history. In fact, when discussing this bird with him, when we were both watching it on the water, he did not agree with me that it is a Manx shearwater. He said he thought it was some sort of diver, one of the Colymbi. . . .

He gave me the address of Major Bingham Crabbe, who, on my writing to him, replied that

from the first moment I saw the bird I have been convinced that it is a guillemot. It is an expert diver, stays under water 1 m. 30 secs. to 1 m. 35 secs., and that's longer than the grebes and ducks which frequent the same part of the lake in large numbers. Its colour is dark chocolate brown and pure white,

legs black, impossible to see if ringed or not. It has a call between a bark and a croak, and seems quite happy and contented
in spite of its wounded wing. It is just the size of a guillemot.
I don't think a shearwater would get a living here as there is no
plankton, whale oil and so on, but millions of bleak which a
guillemot might catch. . . .

I now wrote to a good Swiss naturalist who had visited
Skokholm a year before, and asked him for his help, although
he lived in Berne. With Guggisberg's assistance, about a
month later, the wounded bird was caught in a fishing net.
It proved to be a black-throated diver!

*   *   *   *   *

And after all this fuss—which had led me very seriously
to consider spending Christmas at Montreux—on 30th
March 1938 I recovered EXP 106 in her burrow.

If only she could have told me what she had been doing
in those winter months since she had flown from His
Britannic Majesty's Consul's hands at Venice! But EXP
106 was quite unmoved by my conversation. She had
been engaged in lining the old nest when I found her.
She looked sleek and well. She pecked crossly at my
hands.

In that year she mated with her first (1937) husband
RS 2313, and for that matter she is with him to-day.

The other Frensham-Venice bird, RS 2317, who had
returned so successfully last summer, again occupied her
old nest in the following spring. But her husband did
not return—though he was a young bird and had been
on no homing expeditions whatsoever. She therefore
took up with a new mate, a young unringed bird, and is
with him to-day.

By which route these two birds reached home from
Venice was now still a matter for conjecture. If EXP 106
had really been recovered on the Lake of Geneva we could
have supposed that she had travelled by the short overland
route, the lake being on a line drawn direct between

Venice and Skokholm. But all we had established was that Manx shearwaters are able to return when released in distant, almost land-locked, seas previously unknown to them, and hundreds of miles from home, a feat arguing a marvellous 'sense of geographical position,' to quote Riviere's suitable definition.[1]   But, again, what the physiological mechanism of homing is we did not know.

Many friends and correspondents encouraged us to continue the experiments. I had expected some protests from tender-hearted ladies, objecting to the sending of nesting birds abroad. I received no such protests. The only letter which might have been construed as a protest came, curiously enough, from the commander of a British submarine flotilla. While the director of the Edward Grey Institute of Field Ornithology suggested we should complete the experiments, if possible, by releasing shearwaters in the High Alps.

We did so in 1939. For these homing experiments I would not employ any more subjects of the community of the knoll burrows. They and their pedigrees were now too valuable. However there were plenty of shearwaters elsewhere in the home meadow; for the last five years we had been ringing and re-ringing an average of over 300 adults per annum on these seven acres. The only difficulty was to find enough suitable nests and arrange them with observation sods. We required at least 15 nests to select 12 birds from—since we were operating early in the season and not all the birds would have settled down to incubation. As my wife and I were going abroad, much of this work fell on my sister and her husband, John Buxton, who were looking after the island during our absence.

Twelve adults, first ringed in 1937, 1938, or 1939, were taken from eggs in nests in the meadow. They were sent by air to Switzerland. Herr A. Schifferli, in charge of the Sempach Bird Observatory, wrote that they arrived in

[1] *The Homing Faculty in Pigeons.* Verhand. des VI. Orn. Kon. Copenhagen, 1926, and Berlin, 1929.

very good condition. Three were released on a little hill near Basle, nearest point in Switzerland to Skokholm; three were released at Lugano, farthest point in Switzerland from Skokholm; three were released at Andermatt, near the St Gotthard Pass; and my friend, Charles Guggisberg, released three on a snow-covered hillside near Berne.

Guggisberg sent a splendid map with his account of the release of the three birds near Berne. He wrote:

I left Berne at 6 a.m. on 26th May and arrived at my destination at 10 a.m. The altitude of the exact spot where I released the shearwaters is 5,380 feet. There was still plenty of snow up there, about a foot deep in most places, in fact it had been snowing the day before. The weather was very cloudy around the top of the mountain, limiting the visibility to about 150 to 200 yards. There was a fairly strong wind from the north. The condition of the birds was excellent. When I took them out of the box to make a note of the ring-numbers they bit and scratched vigorously. Each bird got a drink of water before I released it. I released AT 324 at 10.05 a.m., throwing it straight up into the air. It flew away in a north-north-easterly direction. AT 322 was thrown up straight, too, and flew away in a north-north-westerly direction. AT 334 was released at 10.15 a.m. I threw it out over the southern slope of the mountain. It flew towards the south for about a hundred yards and then turned towards the west just before it disappeared in the mist. All three birds flew very well, they certainly were not weakened by the transport. They flew downwards for about fifty yards and then won height rapidly. I was very pleased to renew my acquaintance with the Skokholm shearwaters, and I hope the three birds will reach your lovely island safely. . . .

AT 322 returned to Skokholm in thirteen days.

When this was reported to Guggisberg, he wrote:

I am quite sure you are right in assuming that the birds find their way by a sense of orientation, and I should not wonder if all the shearwaters released during the last few years had made for Skokholm almost in a bee-line, only stopping on the way to rest and feed. When I released the birds I had the impression that they were in no doubt about the direction they had to take. This sense of orientation certainly plays the main part during migration—I never could believe in visual orientation, even in birds where adults and young migrate together. . . .

The other two released near Berne have not yet returned to Skokholm.

It is surprising that the three birds released at Basle failed to return, though they were nearest to Skokholm.

Schifferli reported that two of the birds released in the 'upvalley' above Andermatt were recovered in Switzerland, one a little farther up the pass two days later, still alive, and one at Brigerbad, down in the Canton of Valais beside the river Rhône, dead. They were both making westwards, it seemed. The third was never heard of again.

Strangely enough, the three released on the terrace of the Hôtel du Lac at Lugano, farthest away from Skokholm, did best. Two returned, one in ten days, the other in fifteen days.

If we consider that homing is achieved through a sense of geographical position or direction, as Riviere and Guggisberg believe, it is curious that two out of the three successful returns were made from Lugano, farthest point from Skokholm, and which has also the barrier of the High Alps in that direction. Lake Lugano is partly in Italy and is drained by the river Po flowing into the Adriatic. However, for the reasons given in the discussion on the homing of the Venice birds, it is unlikely that the Lugano birds flew down the Po to the Adriatic, and then made their way by sea. It is more reasonable to suppose that all five birds (two from Venice, two from Lugano, one from Berne) felt the 'pull' of Skokholm drawing them to the northwest and they flew approximately in that direction, deviating when weather and high mountains and the attraction of large surfaces of water called for an alteration in course.

A word as to the failures. It was a hard test, and seventy-five per cent of the 1939 releases failed to get back. Evidently not all the birds were equally strong in their homing power, in their ability to fly a long distance over the land as well as over the sea. The same variation in power is noticed in homing pigeons, where less than ten per cent of trained birds are able to home over very long distances.

*   *   *   *   *

A map to show homing experiments with Manx shearwaters

A friend of mine likes to say that he has a good bump of locality. In Chapter XIII I have quoted an airman's opinion that a vestige of the homing sense is still found in man. And I used to believe that I possessed a keen sense of orientation.

Either with age I have lost that sense of direction, or more likely I never possessed such a faculty. At least, I now believe that it was entirely due to external clues that I found my way about at night and in woods and strange country so easily. I was consciously and unconsciously guided by the sun, moon, stars, and the wind, and by familiar terrestrial objects. At sea the direction of the wind and of the swell, and the position of the sun, have served me well when I have had no compass and no sight of land. How lacking in any real bird-like sense of direction I am I first realized when I was caught without a compass on a perfectly windless and swell-less sea in a fog so dense that it was quite impossible to ascertain the position of the sun. On this occasion I wanted to travel north. Visibility was about thirty yards. I 'sensed' that north was in a certain direction and headed the motor boat that way. After a while, suspicious that I was steering in circles, I broke small pieces of cork and threw them into the water, and tried to keep the boat straight by steering on an imaginary line drawn through the corks and the boat. It is, however, amazingly difficult to steer straight at sea without compass or landmark. And the pieces of cork were soon exhausted. After a while we came back on the line of corks, which thus proved to us that we were circling and lost. Occasionally a sea-bird flew past carrying fish, and as these were obviously making for Skokholm (with what wonderful sureness in such a fog!) I orientated by these whenever I could. Eventually we came upon rocks which, looming terrifyingly large in the mist, were not identified at first. Then their shapes became familiar—we had made a course two miles to east-south-east instead of three miles due north.

A friend of mine had a similar experience in dense fog

on a large lake in Lapland.   A party of Swedish Lapps
was with him in a canoe.   These men, who might be
expected to have a very keen sense of orientation from
living a nomadic existence amid the lakes and fells and
tundra, were completely lost when they were out on the
lake in a mist.   There were no natural signs to aid them,
yet they persisted in rowing confidently forward.   My
friend saw by his compass that they were describing
circles.   Nor would they take his advice until the time
when they should have reached the other side had long
since elapsed.   They were amazed when he guided them
by compass to the farther shore.   They did not understand the compass, and were convinced that the evil spirits
of the lake had been working against them.

The experiments with shearwaters failed to explain
the mechanism of homing.   But they succeeded in
proving that untried shearwaters released on both the
south (seaward) side and the north (continental) side of the
highest Alps are able to return to Skokholm.   This is no
mean achievement for a bird which is normally never out
of sight or hearing of the sea.

We have often wondered at the ability of the young
cuckoo (to take only one typical example) to find its way
alone—for the adults have gone ahead by a month or two—
to winter quarters in tropical Africa.   There is nothing
to guide the young cuckoo to the traditional winter
rendezvous of its species, no more tangible explanation
to the human mind than inherited tendencies, impulses,
instinct.   But while the young cuckoo is at least following
this path graven in its brain by inheritance, the shearwater
suddenly released in the Alps has quite a new situation to
meet.   And in its successful return from this strange situation lies proof of the shearwater's amazing homing faculty.
We need no longer wonder that sea-birds are able to return
over the apparently trackless sea and through heavy mists to
their island homes and to their distant feeding grounds.

*   *   *   *   *

There was one other homing experiment in 1939. It was suggested by a friend in the Royal Air Force that he might release three shearwaters from the air over an inland locality. We sent him three shearwaters taken from nests in the meadow. This is the log of his flight, which was over the Stratford-on-Avon district:

Take-off precisely 3.30 p.m., 17th June, reaching 2,000 feet at 3.35. A course of 265° was followed, i.e. almost due west. The plane was stalled so as to reach minimum speed and the first bird (AT 353) was thrown over the left-hand side. The bird fell twenty feet before gathering its wings and was last seen three-quarters of a minute after being released flying approximately west-south-west.

We lost a certain amount of height and at 1,500 feet, about 3.40, released the second bird (AT 187). This bird fell vertically for at least 200 feet before gathering its wings, and was lost almost immediately directly under the fuselage.

The third (AT 1098) was the most successful. It was released at 2,000 feet and gathered flight almost immediately, certainly within 15 feet of the tail planes. The bird was observed for about two minutes during which the typical shearwater flight was noticed, occasionally gliding and at first when flying at a speed far above its normal maximum, the bird dipped first one wing and then the other and eventually climbed about another two hundred feet. When last seen it was heading due west in the direction in which we had set it.

Of course, one disadvantage of this experiment must be due to the speed at which we released the birds. The lowest possible speed which we can reach in a Gypsy Moth is about 50 m.p.h. and then only for a second, and another difficulty is the extremely bad visibility from the observation cockpit, which meant that in the first two instances I lost the bird far too quickly. . . .

The most successful bird (AT 1098) has not yet been recovered. AT 187 was back in twenty days after release. It might have been home earlier, but constant observation at the nests in the home meadow each night was not possible. AT 353 was recovered in the following spring.

CHAPTER XVI

PORTUGUESE JOURNEY

EACH autumn, when the shearwaters left us in September and October, we registered a sense of loss and emptiness. These strange demoniac birds had found a warm place in our hearts. We were saddened when they deserted the village on the knoll and drew away from us on their annual migration. And often I had said: 'If only we could follow them. . . .'

If only we could have followed our ringed birds to Biscay and the waters of the north coast of Spain! How far did they go beyond that, beyond Cape Finisterre? There were reports that the Manx shearwater was nesting as far south as Madeira and its groups of off-islets. Therefore Manx shearwaters must be found in the intervening waters; but likely enough, our Skokholm birds did not reach so far, or otherwise we should have heard of the recovery there of ringed individuals. Nevertheless we itched to see, to handle and study, these southern shearwaters. Would they be very different from our birds?

We had followed the shearwaters as far north as they were known to breed—to the Faroes, and also, on a visit to Iceland, I had seen a large flock off the Westmann Islands, their most northerly breeding station. We had studied them at home, on Skokholm. But southwards of Skokholm we only knew of them from the recoveries of ringed birds and from the homing experiments.

So the idea that we should one day follow them in person to the south, to Spain and Portugal and Madeira, grew on us. I talked it over with my brother-in-law, John Buxton, poet, writer, and ornithologist. Yes, he and my sister—that same sister who had named Hoofti and Toofti—would be delighted to look after Skokholm for the summer, while my wife and I took a holiday abroad in search of shearwaters.

*　　*　　*　　*　　*

Early in June we sailed for Lisbon. I had an idea that we should find shearwaters nesting on the Berlengas, a group of islands not far north of Lisbon which have rarely been visited by ornithologists. Strangely enough it was through Jerry Wright, an acquaintance I had first met on board ship on the voyage to the Faroes, that we got on so well in Portugal. He had been on his way, then, to Iceland on business, buying salt cod, or *klipfish*, for the Portuguese market. He had made his home near Lisbon. Now he met us in his car and drove us straight to Peniche, the little fishing village opposite the Berlengas Islands.

From Lisbon a mostly macadam road winds through beautiful hills planted with vines, cork-oaks, eucalyptus, and pines. Donkeys, mules, and oxen pulled carts laden with the June harvest: sheaves of wheat and barley, haulms of beans, bundles of newly stripped cork, faggots of charcoal. In the well-meant effort to please the tourist the Portuguese authorities have planted the roadside verges with geraniums and mesembryanthemums, but almost monotonously so.

At last the dunes of Peniche, and then the narrow cobbled streets, with men in coloured shirts, patched trousers, bare feet, pipe in mouth, nightcap berets on their heads. The women wore shawls and ear-rings, their weathered faces shadowed by a basket of fish or clothes, or by a pitcher, balanced on the head. Innumerable ragged children ran barefoot and shouting after us; they sought to carry our stuff from shop to shop as we hurried (ill-advised word in Portugal) to assemble stores for the visit to the Berlengas. Fruit of all kinds and new potatoes were absurdly cheap. Jerry advised us to buy wine as cheaper and safer than water.

Convoyed by the constable and a customs officer we reached the narrow little haven where the fishing boat Jerry had engaged by telephone was waiting.

I had met Jerry on the boat to Iceland, when I was travelling in search of shearwaters. Now the first man I saw in this remote harbour of Peniche was a Breton fisherman who often visited us at Skokholm, during the course of his brazen poaching for lobsters and crayfish around our island. Yves was more astonished than I was—for I, at least, knew these Breton smacks fished anywhere between Morocco and the Hebrides. We agreed, as we shook hands warmly, that it was a small world. He would have been delighted to take us to the Berlengas, he said, only that he had to be careful not to offend the native fishermen. It was of course forbidden to fish in territorial waters in Portugal as well as in Pembrokeshire, but where could you get fish these days? A man must take a risk. . . .

I smiled as I left Yves. His whole life was one long risk. In his tiny smack he and his mates crossed two thousand miles of sea between St Kilda and Agadir. Poaching only added a relish to the fish pie of his life. . . .

We waved good-bye to Jerry and Yves.

We got off in a Peniche sardine barge, 32 feet long, narrow, clumsy. Once clear of the point, we caught the force of the north wind. The customs officer and another gentleman (he wore a tie, at least), who were making the trip, they said, for the fun of it, may have regretted the lumpy sea. Certainly their faces, which had been red with wine and excitement at the quay, were now green as the heaving waves.

Showers of spray flashed over us. Our huge helmsman received them on his naked chest as he stood with his torn shirt flapping in the wind and his hairy arm over the tiller. 'Pardelas!' he shouted, as a group of great shearwaters skimmed past. I recognised this gannet-like, browner-backed edition of our Skokholm shearwater; it was *Puffinus kuhlii borealis*, the North Atlantic great shear-water. Very likely it was nesting on the Berlengas. We should see.

I jumped to my feet as some smaller shearwaters skimmed past in the distance. But the sun was now sinking behind the black crown of the largest island, and it was too difficult in that rough sea to make them out as Manx shearwaters.

The high tower of the lighthouse, standing in silhouette, gave the island a friendlier look. Our barge thumped an echo from the shadows of the east cliff. We drew in towards some steps below an old fortalice built on an out-lying rock.

Morgado the keeper, resident here for twenty-three years, accepted us with upraised arms, a torrent of dialect, and a smile on his sun-wrinkled face. We had expected the island, except for the lighthouse keepers, to be un-inhabited—but we were glad of the comfortable room in the roofed part of the fortalice, which had beds, chairs, and, surprisingly, a water closet that functioned. . . .

Morgado, like some knight brought up in a good tradition, was solicitous but not servile. He invited us to supplement our Peniche hamper with helpings from his bowl of macaroni and rabbit. He lit a lamp, for darkness had come with its usual speed in this latitude.

We were supping and talking when a horrible rasping cry rang out over the roof of the fortalice. It came thrice—in long-drawn blood-curdling succession. Between each wail there was an audible but ghostly indrawing of breath. It was just as horrible and exactly like, I thought to myself, the noises which a countryman or a dockside worker makes when assembling phlegm.

Morgado watched us with a keen smile. But we were not to be deceived so easily. That wonderful cry could only have been that of a shearwater, we agreed—the pardela had beaten our humble little cocklolly, the Manx shearwater. We finished our meal in haste, and picking up torch, note-book, and wire leg-hooks, we walked across the drawbridge and thence, by a narrow unfenced stone arch, reached the main island.

Have you ever had to tackle 150 steps, each twelve to fifteen inches high? If so, you will agree they should only have been planned by a lunatic or a humorist. These breathless stairs led by zigzags to the plateau. Half-way up, at the entrance to a cave, I nearly caught my first great shearwater as it sat for a moment with the torch lighting up its great yellow bill, brown eye, white breast, and grey-brown back. But it took wing in time, and with that same wild mocking cry floated off into the night.

We had a long and tiring scramble in the dark around the whole coast, exploring each cliff and ravine of the island. It was all very disappointing: the rock too solid to provide many holes, and even in the valleys, where there were pockets of earth, there was no trace of life save the numerous sandy-coloured rabbits and squat brown rats. There were no small petrels (the rats had doubtless seen to that), or Manx shearwaters, only the occasional insane mocking wail of a passing pardela. We had but one good moment—when our torch dazzled a yellow-legged herring-gull among the giant sea-pinks. Before it could make off I had it. I ringed it. It is a bird which has the voice of a British herring-gull and the plumage and leg-colour of a pale lesser black-backed gull.

We returned rather wearily to the fortalice in the small hours.

By day the island was vivid with its yellow rock splashed with grey and orange lichens, and bright with bugloss, thrift, samphire, solanum, knotgrass, figwort, blue pimpernel, and foxglove, to name some of the English-looking flowers which we saw. Most of these were of a fleshy drought-resisting type to suit the arid climate. In the shelter of the east-facing cliffs were giant aloes and figs, and here flitted family parties of black redstarts. A migrating Alpine swift showed its white breast high overhead, while ravens and a kestrel hovered almost motionless in the fresh northerly breeze. The island is much like Skokholm in shape, but it is higher. Its stony crown was occupied by grasshoppers and innumerable lizards, including a few of the giant green species. There was a family of black rock-thrushes here. The coastal slope was the territory of the yellow-legged herring-gulls, and on the inaccessible north-facing cliffs were shags and several colonies of common guillemots.

Our more systematic exploration of the cliffs by day at last yielded a single pardela or great shearwater incubating in a crack under the foundation of the lighthouse fog-signal pipes. A bird with such a frightful yell was evidently not unduly sensitive to the screech of one of the world's most powerful sirens. Perhaps, as Doris said, they compared notes on foggy nights.

The pardela defended its large white egg with stabbing black-margined yellow bill. I grabbed its thrust-out neck and, holding its wings, securely held it while my wife put a ring on its leg. This shearwater is as big as a shag and can give a severe wound with its hooked bill. We returned it to the nest. Both egg and bird later disappeared, stolen by fishermen.

When we got back to the fortalice we found the harbour filling with fishing boats. One after another the graceful lateen sails glided to the landing place. The fishermen were returning from the mainland market. They settled their humble possessions in the ruined parts of the fortalice. They pottered about the courtyard, ragged, unshaven, barefoot, making and mending their nets and crayfish pots, cooking fish over a fire of dried herbs, and some stretched out asleep in the sun. The ancient look-outs and gun embrasures have been converted by the fishermen into rough homes where they can eat, sleep, and shelter from the sun, their privacy from all but the rats assured by an old sail draped over the entrance. A little bread, fish, and wine is all they need, but they supplement this as often as they can with rabbits and pardelas, both of which may

The fortalice in the Berlengas Islands

also be sold profitably at Peniche. In their search for the edible and saleable these men flogged the island as mercilessly as they fished the sea, beginning at low-water mark, where they speared cuttle-fish and conger eels, and collected the smallest limpet, sea-snail, and crawling life, and ending up with the unfortunate birds and rabbits—even rats were not despised as bait for the pots.

The Government-salaried lighthouse keeper, who later guided us on another search for pardelas, was ready to collect everything he could reach, too, and to throw stones at those he could not. The one pardela he found for us disappeared next day. He was wildly excited at every rabbit that sprang up before us, and he ran after it—vainly, of course—shouting with childish glee. Rabbits in Portugal have a close season, but this was not observed on the Berlengas, where every one was gunning and stoning them. This man was one of eight keepers in charge of the powerful light and signal apparatus. They and their families are the only permanent inhabitants of the island, apart from Morgado on his outlying fortalice. I could count thirty children of all ages playing in the sunlight about the lighthouse buildings; these children have no schooling beyond what their parents care to give them. The island, said the keeper, swarmed with migrating birds in spring and autumn. These, with the pardelas, were so often killed at the lantern on misty nights that this had to be protected with a screen of iron bars, against which the larger birds might kill themselves without damaging the glass.

The delightful warmth and colour of the island could not for us offset the feeling of being in a slaughter house. Wearied by this state of affairs (but not unmindful of the poverty of the fishermen which forced them to make unrestricted use of every natural harvest) we retired to watch the shags and guillemots, which seemed to be comparatively safe on the ledges of the overhanging cliffs. The Berlengas are the southernmost breeding ground of the

o

common guillemot; we estimated about 6,000 pairs altogether. A careful count with the glasses of 950 individuals showed that none wore the white bridle over the eye. As I have said earlier in this book, at Skokholm ·5 per cent are bridled, in the Hebrides 15 per cent, in the Shetlands 25 per cent, in the Faroes 40 per cent, and in the Westmann Islands (Iceland) I found some 75 per cent bridled. So that it may be said that the higher the latitude the greater the percentage of bridled birds.

Each night we trudged over the rocks, looking for Manx shearwaters, but hearing only the elusive wail of the pardela. Even these were hard to find at the nest, and at first we had two blank nights. Then at last we traced a small group nesting under a mass of boulders on the north-east shore. Only by painful wriggling deep into these was it possible to get at and ring in three nights a dozen birds, of which three had large white eggs. In those three nights two of the eggs were incubated by the same individuals, but the third egg was sat upon by two birds, indicating (roughly) that though incubation is by both sexes, one bird may sit for two or three days at a stretch. As in the case of the Manx shearwater.

It was bad luck that only on our last night did we discover a low cave in the cliffs of the south-east peninsula. Into this we could just crawl on hands and knees. It opened out twelve feet wide in places but was nowhere high enough for us to stand erect. We crawled for about forty yards until we were completely through the isthmus by this underground passage, and had arrived at a hole, an outlet, in the sheer cliff. A cool breeze hissed through from the west. We could see the lights of the sardine boats burning large and without reflection on the ruffled water. Men were singing out there as they hauled their nets under a star-filled sky and a bright moon setting. In the vault behind us pardelas were wailing.

The earth floor of the cave was beaten hard by the webs of the great shearwaters, but no human foot save ours had left a mark. We hoped the cave was unknown to the fishermen. We caught and ringed thirteen birds as these sat incubating on little platforms of small stones. Crouching against the wall we switched off the torch and waited for the birds to resume their activities undisturbed by the beam of light.

For a while there was no movement. Then a shearwater came shuffling in from the west entrance. A flicker of the torch revealed that he was carrying a sizable stone in his wicked-looking bill. We saw that nearly all the eggs of the pardelas had been laid on little platforms of small stones, raised above the earth floor. Of course, there was no evidence that these platforms were intelligently planned. More likely they were built by an instinct inherited in the species. Any young bird, isolated from hatching hour and brought up artificially, without sight of its nest, will build the nest of its species perfectly if and when able to breed in captivity; this has been demonstrated even with the elaborate nest-builders — with caged weaver-birds, for instance. The stone platforms of the North Atlantic great shearwater, as we saw them in that cave on the Berlengas, might not have been planned with a conscious purpose by the builder, but they were very useful in preventing the large and rather round egg from rolling away.

Outside once more, on the east shore, the sea was still enough for a star to leave a white path on the black inshore water. Slowly the sky reddened over the mainland. We went down those humourless steps to the fortalice. The fishermen were already preparing breakfast, having spread their salted clothes to dry in the courtyard. They called a greeting and we replied. The boat was nearly ready to take us back to Peniche.

We said nothing as to our secret cave. Long may you live in peace there, pardela.

*   *   *   *   *

Thereafter, every island we visited off the coast of Portugal, being for the most part nearer the mainland, proved even more disheartening. No pardelas, no petrels, no Manx shearwaters, and hardly any other birds. Everything was hunted, shot, robbed, or killed down. There were collectors, too, supplying museums and zoos. It was brought home forcibly to us that these institutions are far too unconscientious about how their specimens are secured. Does even the Zoological Society of London inquire fully into the methods of its collectors and agents? Does it, too, compete with other zoos for the possession of rare birds? A curse, we cried, on all zoos, for robbing the pleasant countries and the open spaces of the world of their rarest and loveliest creatures.

A list of 'predatory' birds shot in Portugal, published in the Lisbon daily papers, included every kind of large bird. Rewards were being paid for this indiscriminate slaughter. Thousands of useful birds of all species were being killed or captured, with boastful enthusiasm and by every conceivable means.

Back at Lisbon, we took the only available boat, at this off-season, for Madeira—the German *General San Martin*. She had a mixed freight for South America which included a party of nuns and some Jews expelled from the Reich. She also had a heavy list to starboard which was particularly aggravating in our (starboard) cabin. The nuns used a guitar to accompany their evening praises. The Jews, herded in the lower class, talked together eagerly. Both parties were evidently anxious to get to the new land of South America.

Madeiran fork-tailed petrels—at sea they look scarcely larger than our storm-petrels—danced over a sea that was more than cobalt; it was blue-black as we approached Funchal. Flying fishes rose into the trade wind and glided like mechanical toys, their wings stiff and iridescent in the sunlight; then, losing height, they plunged into the thick blue hillocks of the sea.

Away to the south of Madeira stood the bird islands on which I hoped to find Manx shearwaters, the grim Desertas, brown, barren, immensely rugged and tall, dwarfing some sailing ships under their lee.

To the north the terraced gardens and red-roofed homes of Madeira covered the steep escarpments of the island from sea-level to where the green of pines vanished at 2,000 feet in long garlands of cloud drifting from the north-east. Above this curtain the 5,000-foot pinnacles of the sierra seemed detached and unreal—as unreal as the rumour that on those heights both pardelas and Manx shearwaters were nesting. But we intended to find out.

CHAPTER XVII

THE SIERRA

ENGLAND, the well-named English consul, met us at
Funchal, and took us to see Coelho, the breezy Portuguese
business man who rents the Desertas 'just for the fun of
the thing, for experiment like you at Skokholm, for camping with my family, and for shooting a rabbit or two. Why,
even my name is rabbit—*coelho*, Portuguese for rabbit.
I'll fix it for you, I'll fix everything for you to stay on the
Desertas. Only give me a few days to get the stuff and fix
a boat ready for you. You have a look around Madeira,
and rest up ready for the tough life out there. . . .'

Coelho waved his hand comprehensively towards the
brown islands lying south-east of Funchal. He was reassuring, confident.

This suited us. There would be time, not for a sight-
seeing trip in Madeira, but for a journey into the mountains, where I hoped to find shearwaters nesting in the
rocks of the sierra.

We packed a tent and some food and left secretly,
ashamed to admit our unusual object, and ashamed to say
how glad we were to escape tourist-crammed, pedlar-
infested Funchal, with its daily influx of luxury cruising
liners. We had one look at the local museum and were
pleased to see specimens of Manx shearwater nestlings
labelled as having been taken in the sierra. Then we took
a car as far as a car would go along the mountain road.

We dismissed the car and walked on to the edge of the
Curral das Frieras, a tremendous volcanic chasm surrounded on three sides by unclimbable green walls rising
three thousand feet from its cultivated floor. Far above
was the Pico do Ariero, the highest sierra, amid whose

barren screes (as we judged from the map) shearwaters would be nesting, if they nested anywhere in Madeira. The immediate prospect was not cheering, however; the cloud cap was close overhead and it was already sunset, conditions which shearwaters might enjoy, but not good enough for us to start a stiff five-mile scramble over unknown mountain. We had better camp and explore the ground in the morning, ready for a long night with the birds, following the location of the breeding ground.

Where the pines ended and sheep-walks began, we found a small cave with crickets singing and a rill leaping from the rock itself. Nothing could have been more convenient. We made camp within the cave, and had our supper.

To the noise of the crickets was presently added the singing of peasant voices. It was uneven singing. The words lurched drunkenly. I shut my note-book. It was too dark to write more anyway. And the voices were drawing nearer, up the path which ran towards the mountain, past the entrance to the cave.

Four peasants stumbled along, saw our camp, stopped, shouted greetings, and hearing our English accents in reply, came inquisitively forward. Quietly I cursed their discovering us, and, loudly, wished them a good journey. They were going to the higher part of the Curral das Frieras. Would the senhor and senhora join them? It would be interesting. . . .

The leering, drunken look of the ringleader convinced me that such a journey would be interesting, at night . . . with that narrow path alongside the precipices. Alone, yes, I might have taken the road with them, but not with Doris, not at such an hour.

I explained as best I could in the few words of Portuguese that I remembered, using gestures as well, that we were in search of birds. Did they know where the pardela nested? Was it on the Pico do Ariero? I indicated that I had no desire to accompany them that night, but perhaps they could guide us to-morrow? They seemed not to understand, deliberately. . . .

Eventually I got them moving up the mountain path, talking to them quietly, and edging them along. They all carried heavy mountain staves. They smelt of wine, sweat, and garlic, and one looked, in the half-light, cunning and evil.

Doris, back in the tent, was trying to sleep.

I left them stumbling reluctantly upwards. The moon was up, but the valley was still in shadow when I got back into the cave.

I had hardly settled in the tent before the peasants were back. They drank noisily at the fountain—so noisily that I knew they were making this an excuse to return and molest us.

We had not long to wait. Our ignoring them entirely produced a well-aimed stone upon the green canvas covering us.

I got up angrily. I marched up to them and told them that my wife was sleeping . . . 'senhora somno,' and that if they did not 'vamos' there would be the 'Policia de Funchal' to be reckoned with.

The ringleader held out his palm and rubbed it significantly. Another lifted his elbow, signifying a drink might not be out of place. But I was too cross to bother with them any longer. With one last promise that I would consider paying for guides to-morrow, I hustled them bodily back up the path to the mountain.

It is easy to put all this down on paper now. But let me admit that my heart was uneasy. I felt that this was not the last time I should encounter them that night. They had moved onwards with the greatest reluctance and mutterings. Perhaps I ought to have entertained them and make merry with the one bottle of local whisky I had bought in Funchal? It would have been better if I had been on my own.

We had no weapons beyond a small hammer and a

powerful torch. But I immediately prepared for the worst
by laying a trip wire across the mouth of the cave, lashing
the ends to a can of water and a drum of paraffin. We
packed our valuables, too, but laughed at our precautions
as we did so.

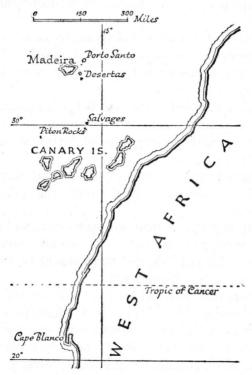

A sketch map to show the position of the Desertas and Salvages

But we had not finished packing before there was a
scraping noise as one of the peasants returned, this time
coming *up* the hill. I was not in the least deceived by
this roundabout return. I stood quite still in the back of
the cave waiting for him to trip over my wire. Unfortunately he dropped to his knees and began to crawl towards
the tent. Possibly he thought we were asleep inside. He
could not see me in the darkness of the cave, but I could

see him well as he moved, outlined against the night sky in the entrance of the cave.

He was joined silently by two others. The fourth had evidently decided not to show himself, for I did not see him again in the fight that followed.

It began with the flashing of my torch upon them. Discovered, they began throwing stones at the tent and at me. The ringleader rushed forward at the light, but tripped over the wire, and as he fell headlong, I was able to snatch the staff out of his hand. I used this to beat off the others while Doris, at my bidding, removed the camera, the case with our papers and documents, and the *aguardente* (brandy), and the one bottle of wine. She clung to the bottles, intending, as she said afterwards, to use them on the heads of the robbers, if they came too near. She hid the valuables in the trees beyond the cave, slipping out unobserved in the darkness while I kept the three men at bay with the bright beam of the torch and the whirling staff.

The powerful light of the shearwater torch was perhaps our salvation in that tight corner. One is quite blind for a while after looking into the beam. Using it always on their eyes, I could move about behind it and dodge stones and staves. I could break one staff on the shoulders of one man, and then snatch the staff of another. We were now equal in weapons, except that the two staffless men could still grope for and throw stones. But they were too cowardly to throw themselves bodily at me. . . .

Once the valuables were safe there was nothing to do but to back away, carrying the box of our clothes, and leaving only the tent and the food. I cannot easily account for the calmness that filled me after the first onslaught, but I see now that I fought with discretion. I could easily have laid out at least one of them with a blow to the head, but I used the staff solely on their bodies, thinking, I suppose, that if I stunned one the others might have laid me out, and then perhaps Doris might have

suffered. . . . And I remember especially my annoyance
that the whole expedition after the shearwaters was likely
to be spoiled.

It was—for a while.   The three peasants did not attempt
to follow us—it was the spoils that they were after.   We
had time to move the valuables still farther down the road,
and to mark the new place where we had hidden them.
Then we had a weary trudge downhill to the nearest
telephone.

This happened to be some four or five miles away, at
the sanatorium or madhouse of Trapiche, an establishment
run by monks.   I had to scale the great iron gates and ring
long at the door, for it was past midnight.

At last a side door opened cautiously.   I said, 'telephon-
policia-Funchal' in one breath, so as to give the impression
of urgency, though as a matter of fact I was quite cold with
waiting.

The lay brother was dubious.   He didn't like the look of me
by moonlight, clearly.   He waved his hands, bidding me stay
outside, and he went back, locking the door behind him.

Presently he opened the main door and took me to the
telephone.   He had no English, and it was some minutes
before he could get through, not to the police as I had
asked, but to the British Consul.

This weary official (not our friend England, who had
lately retired from the post) clearly did not want to be
bothered with us at this time of night.   He thought the
establishment from which I was speaking was a suitable
place for us to stay the night.   We had better remain until
the morning.   I refused, saying that I intended getting
a car somehow, so as to get my valuables back and to get
my wife down to Funchal.   He said that he was very tired,
he had been to a diplomatic function that evening. . . .

I rang through to Coelho, reluctantly, because I did not
want to disturb him so late at night.   He, good soul,
immediately said he would come up to Trapiche in a car,
bringing everything necessary.   He would 'fix it.   I'll

fix the ——— blighters. Stand by until I come.' He had
scarcely rung off before the British consul came through
on the phone. The British consul had arranged a car for
us, after all. I'm afraid I took a small, rather malicious
pleasure in replying abruptly: 'Well, cancel it, you're too
late!' and shutting down the receiver.

Coelho came up the mountain road at a furious pace,
with his wife, a young man, and the driver. There was
some doubt whether we could proceed farther up the
mountain track in so large a car. But we had a daring
and skilful driver, who negotiated the hairpin bends and
thought nothing of driving along the edge of the precipices
with the mudguards, and almost the wheels, in space. This,
in the darkness, guided only by the powerful headlights, was
more nerve-racking than the affair at the cave itself.

Our valuables were still in safe hiding, but the rest of the
camp was looted and the robbers gone. My binoculars,
which in the excitement I had quite forgotten, were lying
untouched under the grass. We packed the camera, the
clothes, and papers into the car and returned to Coelho's
house in Funchal.

Coelho plied us with tea, wine, bread and butter, home-
cured pork, and a vast amount of talk until we were nodding
with repletion and sleep.

*   *   *   *   *

It was late when we started out for the mountains next
day. My heart was still set upon finding the Manx shearwater in the high sierra. And Coelho, who said he was
not quite ready to send us out on the Desertas trip, gave
us an introduction to a priest who would secure us reliable
guides for the Pico do Ariero.

It was sunset as we passed the Cave of the Purple
Fountain (as the place was called in the newspaper reports
of our adventure. The police had been smart; after a two
days' chase they caught the peasants in the mountains).
Buzzards mewed and a few of the small dark Madeiran

swifts soared with kestrels in the updraught from the
Grande Curral. Three thousand feet below us the dry
crater with its scattered peasant homes was free of cloud,
but the rest of Madeira below us was hidden in a white
mist. As we climbed, a warm north wind stroked our
faces gustily. The moon, waxing beyond the quarter,
saved our torches. At first Funchal and Pilot, the dogs of
our shepherd guides, chased the sleepy grasshoppers that
flew from the dry, slippery mountain grass, but they were
soon tired enough to walk quietly at heel.

Along the west edge of the mountain we walked in file
on the narrow path above the Curral. The crater was
more terrible at night, a bottomless shadow from which
came a cold wind, hissing in the shapes of the rocks. We
were glad when the path twisted back to the moonlit
breast of the mountain. Great boulders and stones
blocked the path here. There was no vegetation at this
height. We searched under the stones for signs of shearwaters. There was none.

From the top of the Pico we seemed to be on a desert
island. We looked down upon and were surrounded by
gigantic billows of cloud, magic but cold under the grey
light of the moon. Over these waves of mist would the
shearwaters come screaming home to the arid crags, as
they came screaming home to Skokholm over the more
solid waves of the sea? We longed to hear their familiar
cries. But as we stood and listened we heard nothing but
the sterile sighing of the wind in the stones, the shepherds
breaking their biscuits, and the crunching of Funchal and
Pilot after fleas.

The worst part of this journey was our inability to make
our wishes quite clear to the shepherds, who spoke Portuguese only and that with a strong country accent. I think
this lack of understanding gave them the excuse to stop
presently, in a wild moraine leading precipitously into the
Curral, and, by sitting down firmly, to indicate to us that
there was no use, point, or safety in going farther than

this agreed place to which the priest had asked them to guide us.

The moraine seemed a likely place for shearwaters, but the shepherds refused to enter it. My wife and I searched it as best we could. It was a slippery and dangerous place, sure enough, but full of promising holes.

There was absolutely no sign of bird traffic, neither footprints nor droppings.

The guides had intimated that 'the birds sing from midnight to three hours,' and we waited by the edge of the moraine, getting cold and giving up hope.

I began to think that we were too late in the summer; that probably in so mild a climate the Manx shearwater nests very early. It could not be numerous, anyway; very likely the peasants kept them down as efficiently as the gone-wild cats and ferrets of Madeira must do. But I liked to speculate on the morning and evening flights of the shearwaters over the wonderful cloud mass to the mountains. I longed to see the birds rising from the sea and soaring up to clear the mists at 4,000 feet, before flying in to their holes beneath the boulders. To believe in that mountain flight was no longer difficult, now that our own birds had homed so successfully when released at Venice, and in the Alps. In a later chapter I describe how I saw a great flight of shearwaters rising from the sea and coming inland over an island before the sun had set; but of course that particular island was not mountainous; it was as small as Skokholm.

Pico do Ariero! Highest mountain in Madeira, and lovely indeed by moonlight. But I wished I had brought warmer clothes. It was past midnight—and still no sign, no cry, of a bird.

What, I wondered, is the fate of the nestling shearwater in these crags when, as is the habit of the species, its parents desert it? It cannot fly from the ground, and it cannot possibly scramble twenty or thirty or forty miles down to the sea through the thickly populated terraces of the coast region. If it ever succeeds in getting away, I thought, it must first tumble into the chasm of the Curral. There perhaps a merciful updraught may help it to find its wings, may help it to use them sufficiently to make a long flapping glide downwards to the sea.

Even on the long march home, by a route direct over the mountains to Trapiche, we heard nothing. The moon set. Darkness and a warmer air wrapped us as we decended. The only paths in the mountains are beside the *levadas*, the concrete channels which conduct the mountain water to irrigate the gardens of Funchal and the coast. Following these we came to the pine belt, and then to the peasants' holdings, with their rich whiff of newly worked earth, of vines and fruit. We heard again the singing of crickets and the barking of watch-dogs.

Waiting for us at the madhouse was another monk, a Lisbon man recently returned from California. We were to make ourselves 'arrome right now'—with coffee and a bed on the reception-room floor.

We dozed for a few hours. Doris complained of a flea—very likely, I thought dreamily, one of Funchal's or Pilot's.

Soon there was a knock at the door. Breakfast was ready and 'the diligence is at the gates; but sure, it 'll wait for you right now.'

Our good host from California looked in at us with a benevolent smile. We must remember to write to him when we got back to London, we sure must, he pleaded.

Perhaps he found the madhouse a little lonely after Lisbon and Los Angeles.

It was a glorious morning. Blackcaps sang in the sugar canes and the pines. Grey wagtails darted among the flowers and fruit and cabbages in the terraced gardens below the windows. The madhouse looked out over the whole of the ship-filled Bay of Funchal.

The driver of the bus tooted his horn once more.

Perhaps away there in the south-east, among the fantastic peaks of the Desertas, we should find the elusive shearwaters?

CHAPTER XVIII

THE DESERTAS

THE redoubtable Senhor Alfonso Coelho was still talking when we went aboard the steam tender he had procured for us at Funchal. Hare, guinea-fowl, partridges—these were among the creatures which had been let loose on the Desertas from time to time—oh, yes, and cats. Fishermen thought it unlucky to drown cats, and so they threw them ashore on the Desertas 'all alive-O!' shouted Coelho, as the boat moved off.

We waved good-bye from the barrel, the water-carrier, the stove, the charts, the pile of provisions, which this grand Madeiran friend had assembled for us. Even a Man Friday had been thrown in, a dark-skinned grinning fisherman from the wild north coast of Madeira.

There was nothing in Funchal harbour to betray the savage north wind which met us offshore. The little boat fairly soused herself in the intense blue water. Hatches were battened down. We willingly gave up our fragmentary breakfast to the fishes. An occasional swift, common tern, and yellow-legged herring-gull glided past us, and we looked at them dully, acutely conscious of the wisdom of those who stay at home. We wallowed slowly towards the Sail Rock, a detached finger north of Chao, the northernmost of the three islands of the Desertas.

When we had gained some degree of shelter under Chao's west shore we sat up and studied the splendid flight of the North Atlantic great shearwater. On the Berlengas this bird had been called pardela; here the fishermen knew it as the cagarra; both titles are probably derived from its harsh call. It rose from the sea simply by

The Madeiran little shearwater nests in the off-islets of Madeira where it finds cover in small and often inaccessible holes

This Madeiran petrel was ringed before being returned to its egg hidden in the rocks on the Desertas

opening its wings and paddling with its feet up the slope
of a wave; there was no flapping—when it got to the crest
of the wave it was automatically launched like the glider
it was.

In a little haven in the south-west of Chao we were quite
free of the trade wind. We tumbled ashore on a narrow
ledge piled high with limpet shells, fish bones, and birds'
wings. Innumerable crabs were crawling in and out of
the water as far as their common frontier with a million
darting lizards which held the higher ground.

Manoel, our thin wiry Man Friday, made no bones
about humping our luggage three hundred feet up a rough
cliff path to the plateau of Chao. This is a desert of about
one hundred acres, covered with stones, dead grass, wormwood and a fleshy green plant with purple flowers, which
we soon recognised as the ice plant, *Mesembryanthemum
crystallinum*. This astonishing plant is completely covered
with transparent globules which burst under your feet,
soaking your sandals with clear water. The hottest sun
does not shrivel the ice plant, though it becomes sticky at
high temperatures. Its value on a waterless desert is
obvious; but rabbits, lizards, and birds seemed to be the
only customers at its fountains on Chao.

A buzzard—darker than our Welsh bird—and a kestrel
floated overhead, and there ran before us the palest pipit
I have ever seen, a bird with a thin little cry and a tendency
to keep running rather than flying.

We hastened to get into a roofless stone hut, the only
building on this uninhabited island. We slung our tent
as an awning above it, in place of a roof. Darkness came
swiftly. The lizards retired—we had barely succeeded in
keeping them out of the soup.

As we ate we heard the noises of small petrels. The
now familiar sobbing wail of the great shearwater, distantly
from the cliffs; and nearer, a quiet 'whok' from the
heaped-up stones—this later proved to be the single note
of the 'alma negra,' Bulwer's petrel, a completely black

P

wedge-tailed bird as large as a mistle-thrush. Then a noise like a finger rubbed on a window-pane—this was the note of the Madeiran fork-tailed petrel, a bird not so very much larger than our Skokholm storm-petrel and with very similar habits; in fact this bird uttered occasionally, along with the window-pane squeak, a typical storm-petrel-like purring—from crevices in our stone hut.

Excited by these noises, we lit a pressure lantern which Coelho had given us, and spent the night stumbling over the desert, hoping to locate our own Manx shearwater as well as the rare soft-plumaged petrel (*Pterodroma mollis feae*), of which so little is known except that it is found occasionally breeding in the Desertas.

Strange to say, this lonely desert island was at one time colonized by hardy emigrants, and the land divided into vineyards. The gathered stones lay in heaps and ridges—against which we constantly bruised our legs—making ideal homes for the nesting petrels. Bulwer's petrel was everywhere. We marked a dozen nests near the camp, ringing the incubating adults, and numbering the single eggs. But other birds were comparatively scarce.

In a black ravine on the north side, deep among the debris of the cliffs, we found the shrivelled body of a Madeiran little shearwater, a bird like our Manx shearwater but with blue legs and scarcely so large as a starling. We hooked out several great shearwaters or cagarras which were courting in these labyrinths, but it was clear, from the numbers of wings lying about, that the fishermen had taken as heavy a tribute here as at the Berlengas. The cagarra made a substantial meal for a hungry fisherman—the smaller petrels were too small a mouthful, and so largely escaped molestation. Even the eggs of the cagarras were taken.

We scrambled right down to the water-line in this ravine. The high surf from the trade wind thundered on the black rocks and drowned all finer sounds. Our hurricane lamp was swamped by a sudden cloud of foam. Disappoint-

This large all-black petrel is common in the Desertas. Known as the 'Wroc' from its barking note, it is the Bulwer's petrel of science

Deserta Grande viewed from plateau of Chao Deserta

ment in our hearts—the only breeding bird we had found
was Bulwer's petrel—we climbed back to the camp.

The news of our arrival seemed to have been broadcast
among the fraternity of lizards.   In the morning a hundred
thousand were crawling over and about us.   They ran
along the tent wires overhead, they leaped like grasshoppers where they could not climb, they rained down
on us when they found themselves skidding on our green
canvas roof, and they ran in and out between the folds of
our sleeping bags.   Already they were deep in our pro-
vision chest.   The fruit was a seething lump of black
forms.   A clap and a shout and they all rushed for cover—
only to come stealing back like a lot of naughty boys on
tiptoe.   We found we could only keep them at bay by
violent movement and shouting.   What they lived on
when no humans were camping here was a mystery to me;
we were said to be the first campers in ten years, too.
When a lizard was full-bellied it lay sluggishly in the sun,
its four 'hands' raised in the air with gastronomic complacency.

We had to cover everything down tight, almost air-tight,
and even then our food was not free from the greatest
curse of this latitude, the Argentine ant, a minute insect
which nothing but low temperatures can daunt.   Chao had a
pleasant average shade temperature of 74°, due to the cool
trade wind which never ceased to sweep the island.

At the landing place Manoel shamed our timid dives
with beautifully executed swallow-flights from cliff to sea.
He had already caught our breakfast—a string of gaudy
rock fishes, which fried out deliciously.

So we breakfasted at noon, and lay on our wormwood
couches watching the lizards for some hours.   We were
going to attempt the ascent of the Deserta Grande, the
yellow and purple island lying like a dinosaur to the south
of Chao.   It was too hot to do this by day; and anyway
we wanted to do it at night for the sake of hearing and
locating petrels and shearwaters.

In those hours of rest we began to like Chao. We saw Manoel vainly trying to stalk and slay with stones the rabbits which slipped before him through the stones and the wormwood bushes. A small dark swift kept swooping around him, after insects which he disturbed. A kestrel dropped down towards a single butterfly which wavered over the glaring plain. Quite near us we could hear the goldfinch-like notes of the small dull native canaries which were feeding on the seeds of the ice plant.

An hour before the sun dropped into the cloud-capped mountains of distant Madeira we embarked for the Deserta Grande in the dinghy which Coelho had loaned us. We had water, biscuits, and butter. It was an inadequate little vessel, and as we crossed the strait Manoel had frequently to turn the boat head on to waves breaking astern. Scores of great shearwaters hurried past, waiting for the darkness which would enable them to take to the land. A flock of common terns, evidently non-breeders, settled down to sleep on a outlying rock.

We had great hopes of what we should find on the wild heights of the Deserta Grande.

*   *   *   *   *

It did not look possible to land from that dinghy on the surf-pounded rocks, but Manoel manœuvred with a coolness and lack of hesitation which once more shamed us islanders. We got no more than wet feet as we jumped ashore, leaving him to moor the dinghy in the foam at the edge of the surf.

It was now 8.30 p.m. B.S.T., and though it was mid-summer it was already quite dark in this latitude. We lit the pressure lamp and with its brilliant light began the difficult path nine hundred feet almost sheer up a boulder-and-rubble-filled crack in the cliffs. Great shearwaters were moaning overhead, Bulwer's petrels skimmed past and barked from holes underfoot, and the window-pane squeak of the Madeiran petrel startled us occasionally.

But hungrily I longed for more birds, for the sound we had come so far to hear, the wail of our Manx shearwater. No; the Deserta Grande was not a patch on Skokholm's Night Entertainment. Not so far.

Looking back towards the sea, we saw nothing but a cruel blackness into which a false step, a misplaced hand, would throw you; but it was only afterwards that these grim thoughts came to me. My mind was filled with thoughts of birds just then.

At the top we threw ourselves down upon the yellow grass and began to drink, not caring that the water tasted of the barrel and had not been (as we had been warned all water should be) boiled. We were in the stony valley visible from Chao, and which in spring is noted for its lovely poppies. Just now it seemed to us to be a particularly arid corrie, with scarcely any cover for man or bird or beast, and swept by a height-cooled trade wind.

We moved over the yellow land, and as no birds could be seen or heard I began to think I had never seen such a forsaken and desolate spot in all my island journeys. Manoel, however, promised us 'much cagarras' (large shearwaters), as well as 'few pintaidhos' (small shearwaters), so we persevered, taking the cliff edge and skirting the ridge of the island upwards to its high crown. But we had to work hard to catch and ring even four cagarras and three Bulwer's petrels, and it gradually became clear to me that all the birds had been driven to the inaccessible cliff holes by the fishermen. There were plenty of severed wings of the cagarra lying about to prove this slaughter.

Once my heart leaped as I heard a low bleating. Thinking it was the note of the rare soft-plumaged shearwater I rushed forward. A herd of wild goats sprang past in the light of the lamp, and Manoel and Doris laughed. But I got my revenge when Manoel, excitedly working at a hole in which he believed he would find a small shearwater, pulled out one of the miserable dwarf rabbits which inhabit the Deserta Grande.

We pushed on, gradually ascending into wilder and barer country, with the volcanic rock crumbling underfoot. At 1,300 feet there were still to be heard the groans and squeaks of petrels, but I began to be suspicious that these were really echoes from the cliffs. The distant baying of a pack of hounds was traced to a group of Bulwer's petrels breeding in the high rocks. After that there was silence. We had come to a region of naked red granular soil which the ever-present trade wind (never varying much from about four to five strength, Beaufort scale) had torn and twisted into grotesque waves, with here and there a stone perched on a pillar of soil, standing like some monster on sentry-go. Rain, too, had eroded this desert; we were now in the cloud belt, and frosty patches of mist frequently drifted over us.

Manoel seemed more and more unsure of his cagarras and pintaidhos. He moved more reluctantly through the darkness. He led us to a new stratum of soil, covered with areas of bracken and odd clumps of furze. Here, in conditions like those of home, were surely our beloved Manx shearwaters?

The ground was hard, not a hole of any kind, and not a cry, or any sound save that of the wind. We moved on, leaving the bracken and plunging ankle-deep into a loose ochreous earth which the wind stirred up into our eyes. It was hard going, and we seemed to be moving haphazardly.

I got out my compass and studied it.

Manoel was leading us in circles and figures of eight.

Our light was showing signs of collapse, and the wind was bitterly cold. Manoel had clearly lost the way. Probably he was weary of this strange night hunt. I took the lead and struck upwards for the peak of the Deserta Grande. It was long past midnight and time for the shear-waters, if any existed here, to return to the sea.

The mantle of the pressure lamp was breaking, with our rough usage of the lantern. I led the way back to the bracken area just in time before it gave out, leaving us to grope with a hand torch containing almost exhausted batteries.

I had remembered the approximate position of some clumps of furze, and luckily I found them. They were quite dead and would burn well, as they had stems six inches thick. They must have been very old, and how they ever came to grow there is a botanical conundrum to me. But we felt they had not lived in vain as we roasted ourselves, spit-fashion, before the delicious flames.

Manoel never found us his cagarras and pintaidhos, and we never knew if he really meant to or was only trying to earn our admiration for his staying powers and a suitable reward from us, from these two people whom he secretly regarded, as Coelho later told us, as mad. (Who else would climb the Deserta Grande in the middle of the night? Only madmen assuredly! Now that we had done it, we were inclined to agree.)

In the light of morning the Deserta Grande seemed to live a little less austerely up to its name. As we ate our biscuits and butter, a few Madeiran pipits, a single buzzard, canaries, swifts, and herring-gulls were seen over the arid fields of Poppy Valley. Fields, yes—because even here there are traces of a grim colonization, of a considerable cultivation.

Chao, where all our belongings were, now seemed to be a place of charm. When the sun brightened we could look down on the little island, a golden finger in the cobalt sea. Somehow we were glad to be returning there, to be leaving the sterile, cold, birdless main island. But it was not to be left in haste. It is always easier to climb up than down. We had a slow and painful scramble down the thousand-foot-long crack to the tossing dinghy.

After an hour's hard pulling we made Chao landing.

Five lean, ragged, but happy-looking fishermen were eating sweet potatoes and fish in their little boat anchored there. They were enjoying life as much as the Marloes fishermen enjoy camping in their boats in Skokholm's haven.   Two more fishermen had caught a rabbit, and were startled into releasing it as we came upon them in the cliff path.   Perhaps they were aware that we were at Chao by permission of the owner, whereas they were there only by traditional right, which in the circumstances meant that they were poaching, and knew it.   I regretted the rabbit escaping, as I had been commissioned to secure a few of these Chao conies, which are as large as hares, and have

Catching petrels above our camp hut at Chao Deserta Island

black-tipped ears, but breed and dig holes like rabbits. Later we got some with a torch and cudgel at night.   I found their breeding organs completely regressed; it is likely that they only breed in the short period of the winter rains, when the desert flowers again.

We were feeling the strain of the long climb and the night on the Deserta Grande.   Manoel complained of a sore throat, which we pacified with wine and the local fire-water, *aguardente*.   Our own dry throats we slaked with the famous, if soapy, Porto Santo water, each bottle of which bears the legend 'This wather is most certainly one of the beste for affections of the Stomach, the Kidneys, and the Intestine.'

We rested until dusk, then erected a flue-net over the boulders in which our marked Bulwer's petrels were nesting.

This was our plan for the six days we lived on Chao: resting by day, and working by night at my favourite employment.

The island became an increasingly happy place for us as we built up an intelligent association with these handsome black petrels, the only ones breeding accessibly on Chao. The larger shearwaters were either not nesting, or had been driven to the cliff fastnesses by the fishermen. Our Bulwer's petrels had eggs on the point of hatching. By ringing we discovered that both sexes (indistinguishable in the hand) incubated, remaining on the egg for from one to five days at a stretch, and being visited at night somewhat irregularly by the bird off duty. The chicks as they hatched were much more active than our Skokholm storm-petrels, which cannot hold up their heads at first, or open their eyes. The day-old Bulwer's petrels had their eyes open and could move about and even try to climb rocks with hooking bill and wing stumps, if placed in the sunlight. No doubt the high temperatures of this latitude quickens the incubation and growing periods of birds generally. The constant sunshine nourishes all forms of life here which could not otherwise subsist on the basic source of nourishment, the scanty pasture. The nestling petrels are always warm beneath the sun-heated rocks, and at sea all day the adult petrels enjoy almost continuous sunshine.

When thrown into the air from the nest, most nocturnal petrels and shearwaters immediately fly out to sea—the land is unfamiliar to them by day. But all the Bulwer's petrels we released by day flew uneasily over the nesting ground, as if orientating themselves, before suddenly diving home to their own crevice. This was the more surprising because we found Bulwer's petrel to be strictly nocturnal, arriving punctually and filling our flue-net with a rush at about 8 p.m. We constantly caught in the net individuals which we had ringed in their rock homes hard by; suggesting a localized flight, soon over. When leaving later the birds slipped away singly and directly.

Each morning, as it was getting light, we would go down to the landing place for a bathe, just as the last Bulwer's petrels glided to sea like monster swifts. Soon a few real swifts would appear, glancing under the grey cliffs in whose warm niches they had been sleeping. The Madeiran gulls would start to call at 5 a.m., and the terns would stretch their delicate wings from the lower rocks and dance past the landing place, keeping Manoel company in his fishing. Manoel slept in the limpet-shell and cagarra-wing midden with other fishermen who nightly came ashore for the purpose, leaving their little boats moored off. Manoel placed his feet in a sack and dug his shoulders into the midden, and, unheeding the inumerable crabs which explored the dump, slept soundly.

The fishermen would now be stirring, waking reluctantly, for a while hanging their heads between their knees as if in torment, then rising to prepare a breakfast of fish, or a tin of limpets boiled over a handful of wormwood sticks. One ragged old man would never leave his boat. I never saw him eat anything. He would stand up in his boat and talk angrily to the others on the shore. He seemed to jeer at them. But they took no notice of him, and he may have been mad. Two young men would join him after their meal, and the trio would slip off for the day's fishing, the old fellow still talking extravagantly.

CHAPTER XIX

THE SALVAGES

ALFONSO COELHO had said that a small steamer might be sailing for the Salvage Islands during the week. If so he would try to arrange for it to pick us up at Chao on her way south. It is rare for these islands to be visited more than once a year, but at that moment they were being worked by a phosphate company. They lie 180 miles south of the Desertas, and although much nearer the Canary Islands, they are a Portuguese possession. Very few British people have set foot on these scorched acres of volcanic rock. It was questionable whether the Manx shearwater nested there, but great numbers of other petrels did. It had been an old dream of mine to live there—as I had dreamed, when a boy, of living on every such completely remote island: Tristan da Cunha, Jan Mayen, North Rona, Fernando da Noronha, Easter Island, Pitcairn. Impossible dreams, of course.

We could scarcely believe our luck when we saw the steamer approaching Chao at sunrise on the sixth day.

The *Butio* was filled with Portuguese labourers on the lower deck, and on the bridge deck, a sort of hen-coop arrangement with an awning, were the 'passengers,' comprising two priests on an entomological expedition, and one or two business men out for a cruise and a rabbit hunt. We were promoted to the bridge deck.

It was an idle day for us, the steamer rocking gently on a faint blue swell, flying fishes rising and falling before the heavy bow-wave, a line of clean white clouds on the horizon, and very few birds: an occasional cagarra, two sooty shearwaters, and once a Kentish plover circled around the ship. We ate, talked, but chiefly slept.

At 1 a.m. we woke to shouts indicating arrival, by clever piloting, at the unlighted Salvage anchorage. The grinning pilot accounted for this feat with the explanation that the cagarras had acted as a fog signal in the dark. There was certainly the most splendid hullabaloo I have ever enjoyed. Hundreds of thousands of these North Atlantic great shearwaters were screaming about us as our anchor rattled down in a bay, the outlines of which I could not at first discern.

A light flared out from the cliffs in answer to our whistle.

We hastily filled our pockets with rings and went ashore, rowed there by the guidance of a flare which proved to be held by a hairy, wild-looking, half-naked guano-digger, who was backed by a host of his fellows. The scene was unreal, theatrical; but I had no time for reflection on this then. I wanted to spend as much of the night as was left among the birds. The captain of the steamer had said we might have to sail in the morning, if the weather or a swell threatened.

Flashing our torches, we found a path zigzagging upwards, but we had hardly moved a few yards before we stumbled on the cagarras at their night festival. Some were love-making in the pathway, others were skimming over our heads, but the majority were paired off and sitting together in the gas-blown holes of the volcanic rock. As these holes were mostly shallow the cagarras were delightfully accessible for ringing—once you got into the way of handling them without their handling you. Manoel never learned how to do this, and had several severe bites, which, together with his superstitious nature and our queer ways, made him afterwards report to Coelho that he had been ill-used.

We gradually 'ringed' our way to the top of the island, which proved to be comparatively flat. Here was a soft soil covered with the ice plant, which soon soaked our feet. Farther inland, however, it was shrivelled and dry and

'Fairy bird' or frigate petrel (note ring on leg)

The barren rocks of Great Salvage, scorched by sun and salt, nevertheless support great numbers of nocturnal sea birds and are rich in guano mixed with volcanic dust

our feet sank at every other step into the little burrows of the frigate-petrel, a charming white-breasted blue petrel with long legs which gave it in flight the appearance of a huge may-fly.   The adults rose from the ground and danced before us like fairies in the light of the torch, calling with a faint note that had a redshank-like quality, a voice of the spaces.   They fluttered fragilely.   Some became entangled in the groves of the nicotine plant, *Nicotiana glauca*, which in places rose to a height of ten feet.   The frigate-petrels seemed altogether too feeble and too long in the leg to have dug those holes in the hard phosphatic soil.   But as they also seemed too weak on the wing to ride out storms at sea—as they undoubtedly do so ride them—it was a case of appearances being deceptive.   The bird was stronger than it seemed.   It was fighting to maintain possession of nesting holes on this overcrowded island, and fighting successfully, for we found plenty of down-tufted youngsters at fledging age, crawling about at the entrance to the burrows.   Probably these youngsters had been deserted, and, like the young storm-petrel and the juvenile Manx shearwater, were thinning down preparatory for the journey to the sea.   Some of them were very fat, especially the more downy ones.

Every hole in this area seemed to contain life.   Exploring where our feet had broken through we found that some Madeiran petrels had laid eggs, and incubation was just starting—the eggs were almost transparent.   In other burrows the Madeiran little shearwater was sitting without egg or chick, evidently at the courtship, the pre-egg stage. It was clear that the holes were occupied by the three species in turn the year through.   The territorial year is probably divided roughly as follows: the frigate-petrels occupy the honeycomb from April to July (we had arrived here on 16th July), the Madeiran petrels from August to November, and the little shearwater from December to March.   Overlapping must occur; but this division of the year into specific breeding seasons is convenient, is forced

on these three small petrels by lack of suitable terrain elsewhere. It is only on such islands as the Salvages, remote
and generally uninhabited, that there is both freedom from
human interference and a suitable soil for burrowing—in
this latitude. Persecution elsewhere has already exter-
minated several island-breeding species, including some
petrels.

We thought at first that we had discovered the Manx
shearwater on the Salvages. We heard the typical scream,
but it was thinner, higher, more juvenile . . . and then we
discovered that this was the voice of the Madeiran little
shearwater. It was more of a squeal than a scream. It
was uttered by three birds playing and courting together
in a rock crevice; probably two males paying court to one
female. This was a delightful little bird, a toy edition of
our Skokholm shearwater, alike in plumage, but shorter in
the bill and with rich blue legs. I should like to have been
able to transplant some to Skokholm.

In the rocks, too, were plenty of Bulwer's petrels, their
barking became a low undertone to the loud cries of the
cagarras, which dominated the island in volume of sound
as they dominated the scene in their numbers. But we
heard nothing at all of Manx shearwaters.

It was astonishing to find low well-built walls stretching
across the island, and also retaining the soil of the slopes,
as if cultivation had once been attempted, perhaps by a
colonization of Madeirans, or of Canary Islanders, or
perhaps there had once been a penal settlement here. Now
the walls were used to accommodate the cagarras, stones
having been pulled out at regular intervals along the foot
of the walls, and in each hole sat a brooding great shearwater, attended (at this hour of the night) by its mate.
The cagarras were very tame. We could pick them up
and ring them as fast as we could handle them.

The Salvages are an organized cagarra farm. Every
autumn the young cagarras are collected, salted, and taken
for sale at Funchal. They are chiefly eaten by the country

Cagarra or North Atlantic great shearwater on nest

Sunset over Great Salvage Island

folk. Great Salvage Island yields between ten and twenty thousand fledgeling cagarras in September, and some are collected, if possible, from the nearby Piton Rocks. The adults are not molested in any way.

The day was now breaking, but still the cagarras attended to their affairs at the nest, changing the guard, love-making, and caterwauling. The frigate-petrels, the little shear-waters, the Bulwer's and Madeiran petrels, had all vanished at the first grey hint of dawn. It was soon light enough for me to read my notes and light enough for the cagarras to see us and dodge out of our way. Their calling gradually ceased. Yet they were in no hurry to leave. They were still taking flight, leisurely running forward and lifting their great wings into the trade wind, as we walked down to the harbour. The sun was well up before the last had flown. Not so would our Manx shearwater behave; but the great shearwater has nothing to fear from natural enemies on the Salvages, and so it has broken the strict nocturnal rule of the shearwater tribe. Yet in Portugal and the Desertas, farther north, persecution by man has forced this same bird to remain entirely nocturnal.

In the light of day the harbour proved to be a rocky creek edged by walled-up holes and caverns in which lived the thirty or so guano-diggers, and a smaller number of Portuguese fishermen. These homes swarmed with mice and cockroaches and lizards; the stores of food were isolated on smooth pillars and polished tubs up which these pests could not climb. The diggers earned about a shilling a day, and were indentured for four months at a time. They were free men living under convict conditions, but they wore the pleasant smiles of care-free countrymen. After all they had few troubles; they lived simply on maize-meal porridge and fish, clothes were almost unnecessary, and the daily shilling could not be spent, for there was nothing to spend it on. They would return to Madeira passing rich—for a peasant.

Staff in hand, the diggers moved up the slope to work,

to fetch down the sacks of soil, rich in guano and phosphate, dug from the bird burrows. Each man would carry about one hundredweight and a half at a time, resting the sack partly on his head and partly on his shoulders. It was a mile from the diggings to the harbour, where the *Butio's* crew was loading the sacks from small boats.

We went on board, launched our own dinghy (Coelho's, that is), loaded our gear, and rowed around to the south coast—with a parting injunction from the captain to return at the first whistle. He repeated that the steamer would sail at any moment, if a swell started. These swells appear quite suddenly out of a quiet sea, and they can wreck an anchored ship in a few minutes, and they may continue for days.

This south side was a steep moraine of stones and earth, under which were nesting birds, little green and brown geckos, and lizards. Nicotine plants provided a fugitive shade; but luckily, during most of our stay, Great Salvage was covered with vaporous clouds, and the shade temperature did not exceed 80°. We bathed in deliciously cool water.

We could look out, as we breakfasted, at the Piton Reef, whose sandy-looking cone rose from the pale sea about ten miles to the south. We longed—in vain—to visit there.

While we were eating, a fisherman came into the bay. He leaped ashore and began flogging the rocks with the gills of a barracuda. The particles of flesh that were bruised off attracted conger eels, which he swiftly and surely gripped with a pair of rough-edged tongs. He then finished them with a stick.

We climbed about the moraine beyond the camp. The cagarras all had eggs. We marked twenty nests, ringing the sitting birds. We worked upwards through the nicotine groves to the high plateau again. The bridge-deck party had come ashore. The priests, in their flowing robes, were hunting for insects and geckos under the stones.

The others were sniping off the excessively small Salvage rabbit. This animal is scarcely larger than a squirrel, but it proved to be amazingly fat on a diet of sunshine and ice plant.

The surface of the island rises to two high points, leaving depressions filled with the soil which the diggers were sifting and sacking. Burrowed for centuries by birds, it is rich stuff, and it fetches a high price as a concentrated manure in Madeira. Unfortunately, to dig it means turning out the original inhabitants. The adult petrels could, of course, fly off unhurt when discovered by the spade, but their eggs and young were callously thrown aside to wither in the sun, or to be picked up by the very few yellow-legged gulls which haunt the island. These gulls, with the petrel tribe, and some non-breeding common terns, and a pipit which was almost as pale as a white wagtail, made up the bird life of Great Salvage Island.

At noon, as we sat in the fierce sun on the peak of the island, grateful for our wide Madeiran sombreros and the coolness of the trade wind, I was surprised to see two or three cagarras sailing overhead. Soon more arrived. Their numbers increased until there was a splendid assembly of soaring birds. I was even more astonished to see one or two glide to earth and enter their nesting holes.

We sat and watched the magnificent aerial display over our heads. More and more birds arrived, gliding, wheeling, soaring, silent.

By 5 p.m. thousands were wheeling over the island. One or two now gave voice. We went to the edge of the cliffs and saw that rafts of cagarras were gathering on the sea near the shore, too.

The sea and the sky were rapidly filling with cagarras. We had never seen such a wonderful assembly of birds before. This was something that even Skokholm could not compete with. When the clouds became rosy in the west, and the great rafts of cagarras drifted closer inshore,

Q

and their black forms covered the sky over the sea as well as over the land, I can say, at the risk of being sentimental, that a great happiness was mine; that same happiness which Hudson knew when he watched great multitudes of Patagonian birds. The ornithological satisfaction was there, but it was equalled by the pleasure which the background gave, the rich colours of the sky, the sea, and the rocks, and the remote wild surroundings.

But there was more work to do. I wished to ring as many cagarras as possible. Since I had been unable to find Manx shearwaters, I might as well use the one thousand rings I had brought for them on the great shearwaters. It would be interesting to hear later of the movements of these large petrels—if we ringed a good number of them there might be some recoveries which would help to solve the problem of their migration. No one had ringed them before, and the extent of their wanderings was unknown.

We loaded fresh batteries in our torches, and returned to the top of the island by dusk. We fitted up the flue-net over the frigate-petrel holes, but a furious wind came and blew it down. It also began to rain. We retired to a cave in the hill, and took some wine and biscuits, watched with mistrust by some cagarras which were nesting there. Cockroaches and the small Salvage mouse came to the crumbs. The rain soon failed. We returned to our ringing in the shelter of the south cliffs.

The twenty-six hours of continuous work were beginning to tell on us. Manoel had already curled up in the rocks, with his jacket pulled over his head. When Doris suddenly fell asleep with a cagarra in her arms, I realized my own tiredness. We struggled down to the shore, and, finding a stretch of clean gravel in the mouth of a sea cave, we lay down and immediately fell asleep.

*   *   *   *   *

The sun filtered through light clouds into our cave.
To the right was a Bulwer's petrel chick, not above a few
days old, sleeping in an inadequate recess formed by a stone
and my wife's head.   Behind us a dozen cagarras occupied
niches and crevices extending far up into the darkness of
the cave.   The wild notes of their love-making had
merged with the wash of the sea for our lullaby last night.
They were still at it in the sunlight.   I saw the male,
which has a bigger head and bill, nibble his wife's face
delicately.   Confirming our observation at the Berlengas,
I noted that the cagarras had each built a platform of
little stones to retain the egg.   Some of these platforms
were quite substantial, evidently the accumulation of
generations.

We bathed.   I examined the marked nests.   In sixteen
of them the same adults were incubating; in the remaining
four were new (unringed) birds.   Thus we know that each
adult may remain on the nest for at least two days and
nights, and probably longer.   This is the case with the
Manx shearwater, with Bulwer's petrel, the storm-petrel,
and probably all the tube-nosed birds.   The heavy-
headed male cagarras would scream more loudly when
we picked them up—the females only uttered a short
'ka-ka-ka.'

At midday the *Butio's* whistle sounded.   We sent
Manoel on board with our gear, while we continued
ringing.   They were still loading guano, so they could
not be in all that hurry.

It was hard for us to leave that pest-ridden, bird-filled,
arid, dusty, but beautiful island.   We had not half explored
it, even though it was not much larger than Skokholm,
which you can walk around in two hours.   We resumed
our ringing.

Again the whistle went.   We had still five hundred rings
to use up.   I debated the idea of remaining until the
September boat came to collect the young cagarras.   But
then I had promised to be back at Skokholm in August,

to take over from my brother-in-law. And war clouds were gathering; indeed they were breaking already, over Europe. We might be stuck on Great Salvage for the duration of the second world war. It was surprising that this thought did not dismay us more. . . .

We had reached our 708th cagarra ringed when the third and last and angriest whistle of the *Butio* sent us scurrying to the harbour. Everybody was aboard and we could hear the anchor rattling home. A fisherman who was mooring a great open-topped wicker basket containing his catch took us to the steamer as she began lurching out of the haven. The Portuguese are good sailors. This man had just come in from the Piton Rocks. He lived by salting fish during the summer and selling it on return to Madeira in the winter. He would be sailing again the ten miles to the Piton Rocks to-morrow. Yes, he said, there were birds nesting even on that small lonely reef.

We wished we had stayed. But our gear was all aboard, and soon we were scrambling to the bridge deck.

Away in the south a starlike flare marked the dim outline of another fishing boat sailing home from the Piton Reef.

The lights were being lit over the supper table. The bridge deck party was airing its adventures at rabbit shooting, which in this country has all the importance of a tiger shoot. Not even the tragedy of our limpets and rice being, it seemed, accidentally cooked in paraffin instead of olive oil could dishearten the excited hunters. We turned in early, to sleep in our bags on the hard deck.

In the night a Bulwer's petrel brushed past my face, attracted by the ship's lights. I put my hand out, dreamily, and caught it.

It stayed very still while I ringed it. Every one was asleep on the floor-boards of the deck, except the man at the controls. And suddenly I had a great longing to be home on my own island of Skokholm. I wanted to see again the black and white beauties of the knoll village.

Perhaps dear old Caroline was back after all?   If only this bird in my hand had been she. . . .

Well, it would not be many days now.   The boat was headed north, on the first stage of our journey home.   I whispered good luck and good-bye to the little black petrel before I threw it out over the dark water.

Table of Marriages of Principal Characters

Year	Nest A	Nest B	Nest C
1929	Adam & Ada	Bill & Bess	Caroline & Carol
1930	,,	,,	,,
1931	,,	(did not return)	Caroline & ? Carol
1932	,,		,,
1933	(Ada did not return)	Adam & Baby	,,
1934	Baby & RT 9346	Adam & Caroline	**Nest CE**
1935	,,	(Adam did not return)	Caroline & Carol II
1936	(Baby died on board ship)	Carol II & RW 9948	Caroline & Carol III
1937	RS2317 (Venice homer) and mate	,,	,,
1938	,,	,,	Caroline & Carol IV
1939	,,	,,	,,

INDEX